HAUNTED UWHARRIES

GHOST STORIES, WITCH TALES AND OTHER STRANGE HAPPENINGS FROM NORTH AMERICA'S OLDEST MOUNTAINS

FRED T. MORGAN

ILLUSTRATED BY TIM RICKARD

ISBN 0-878086-13-8

Library of Congress Catalog Card No. 92-072657

Printed in the United States of America

Cover design by Tim Rickard
Book design by Elizabeth House

Down Home Press
P.O. Box 4126
Asheboro, N.C. 27204

*This book is dedicated to everyone
who lives in the Uwharrie area
and to all other people everywhere
who love the Uwharries.*

CONTENTS

PART I – GHOST STORIES

PART II – WITCH TALES

PART III – STRANGE HAPPENINGS

INTRODUCTION

From my home I can see a dozen of America's oldest mountains–central North Carolina's Uwharries, remnants of the old Ocoees, which once soared to more than 20,000 feet and rivaled the Swiss Alps of today. But that was hundreds of millions of years and many geological upheavals ago. Now few of the Uwharries rise more than 1,000 feet above sea level. Yet they swell their chests impressively, radiating vestiges of their ancestral luster. For almost the entire 180 degrees of the eastern horizon I can view these hills, from Palmer Mountain rising out of big Badin Lake on the north, to Morrow Mountain, king of this patriarchal clan, on the south.

Pick a day in late October or early November and view these hills when the air's full of wine and headiness, when the sun radiates golden champagne from an azure ice bucket. With fingers of greenery the hillsides mischievously wipe jelly and candy from their cheeks and cloaks. As the westering sun touches burgundy to the broad lip of the sky, the Uwharries pull up a robe of many colors and tuck it around their chins for a night of slumber.

Autumn nights are crinkly cold in the Uwharries. Trees whisper lullabies to the nightlife they shelter. The big moon peers ghostily from a face littered with luminous freckles. Cotton candy clouds resemble phantom schooners sailing across the mysterious deep. Somewhere a pack of fox hounds musically trail their quarry. Frost-tinted air tonics the blood, invigorates the step and spirit, ignites the imagination. Lights in windows glow friendlier and warmer.

The Watchman of the Night spreads coverlets of mist and fog in peculiar layers to shroud his charges. Sounds carry like drumbeats across the crispy night. A falling star paints a fading exclamation mark across the sky in salute to the euphoria of an autumn night in the Uwharries.

A few picturesque brown dirt roads still squirm through these worn mountains. Drive along them. Slowly. Savor the rusticity.

Mule and horse tracks dot the roadway. Grass grows between the wheel paths. A flock of guineas pot-rack raucously. Buzzards rise reluctantly from feasting on a smashed possum. A raggedy rail fence hides under a honeysuckle blanket. A creek murmurs placidly across the road. A four-posted shingle-roofed well shelter lists precariously. An empty log corn crib begs for fat ears. An abandoned hayrake rusts away in a field, its iron claws poised to gouge the earth. A piece of rusty tin roofing squawks a strident protest as the wind flaps it over a crumbling chicken house. Crows screech at an intruding hawk.

If you can manage only a quick one-stop look at the Uwharries, drive to the summit of Morrow Mountain, seven miles east of Albemarle. A little higher than other peaks in the range, Morrow Mountain has been called "The proud Scion of the oldest mountain range on the North American Continent." Here you can view the Uwharries at their grandest.

Five hundred feet below and three crow-flying miles away is the point where the turbulent Yadkin and the wild Uwharrie Rivers join to form the broad-bosomed Pee Dee, which stretches 15 miles to the horizon, thence another 150 miles to the Atlantic.

From Morrow's scraggly dome you can see the surrounding valleys almost as the first European explorers must have seen them in the late 1500's and early 1600's. The explorers were followed by settlers, filtering south from the northern colonies and inland from the Atlantic, some pirate ilk among the latter. That the Indians were reluctant to leave this paradisiacal land which they had inhabited for thousands of years is understandable. Some remained until the Civil War.

The rivers and valleys jealously guard their stories: of lives and fortunes lost and won in taming the Yadkin for hydroelectrical power; of ferry boats and flats; of moonshiner and nature lover Tom

Marks, king of the Narrows, a gorge between two mountains where the wild water raged at its constriction; of fish traps where shad were caught by the hundred pound; of the log courthouses at four county seats, some of which burned under suspicious circumstances prior to 1841 when the western half of Montgomery County was split off at the river to form Stanly County; of activities along the famous Market Road from Salisbury, N.C., to Cheraw, S.C; of the legendary Dr. Francis J. Kron, a physician who ministered to these hill folk for 50 years during the mid-1800's; of the remains of old graveyards, churches, homesteads, fords, grist mills, towns, quarries, springs, roads, and natural formations.

Among these stories, too, are many tales of ghosts, witches, murders, hauntings and other strange happenings ranging from the bizarre to the unbelievable. I first encountered some of this material decades ago while researching an earlier book of Uwharrie ghost tales which has proven quite popular (Ghost Tales of the Uwharries, John F. Blair, Publisher). A few I have known about since boyhood. However, most have been sifted from oral traditions following many a day of driving along Uwharrie byways and coaxing favorite tales from the natives–people for whom I have an awesome appreciation.

It's tempting to take off down a dozen tantalizing side roads and devote more pages to experiences I had while collecting this material. I identify with these experiences as much as with the actual tales. They animate my memory even more. Probably there is enough material here for another book. One of these years, maybe I'll get to write a book about all the absorbing activities related to my exploration of the frontiers of central North Carolina folklore.

Never is a collection of this sort complete. Always there is another good original folk tale lurking somewhere in the Uwharries. Inevitably, I'm always involved in another collection. If, after reading these tales, you become aware of a comparable one from an unpublished source, contact me in any convenient way.

Fred T. Morgan
Albemarle, N.C.
April 4, 1992

GHOST STORIES

LITTLE GHOST, GIANT GHOST

Rafe Hopkins kneed his tired mule along the trail through Caesar's Swamp at the end of a hard day in the fields. By day the swamp was a desolate place. Darkness made it fearsome and now the blackness squeezed in upon the puny flicker from Rafe's lantern.

The mule followed the trail by instinct. Heavy foliage overhead filtered out most of the starlight. Frogs croaked and owls screeched. Crickets yacked. A trace chain jangled as the mule jounced over stones and roots. Occasionally the mule's ears jerked forward as if she had spotted something ahead on the trail.

Abruptly the mule shied so sharply that Rafe would have fallen had he not grabbed the gear. When he quieted the animal and looked ahead, he almost fell off again at what he saw.

Standing on a log beside the path was a baby. not more than a year or two old. The child appeared to be outlined in a soft glow which illuminated him enough for Rafe to see his features. Apparently he was a normal little fellow dressed in white, who looked so appealing Rafe felt he had to speak to him.

"Who are you, little boy, and what are you doing out here in these woods by yourself?" When he got no answer, he continued, "It's a wonder some wild animal hadn't eat you up. I better take you out of this boogery place and find out where you belong."

The little boy lifted his arms toward Rafe. Still mounted, Rafe bent low, grasped the boy, and swung him up behind him onto the mule's rump. "You hold on tight, little man, and we'll get ol' Butter to take us home. You must be starvin' like we are."

Rafe kicked the mule into a trot, but in seconds Butter had slowed to a walk and refused to go any faster. Soon she slowed still more and commenced to blow. Her sides heaved in and out and Rafe could smell new perspiration and feel it under his legs. Never before had the mule failed him. Then he remembered his passenger and held the lantern up to look behind him. What he saw and the tales it generated have reverberated through the Uwharries ever since.

No longer was there a baby on the mule's rump behind him.

Instead, it was a giant!

Rafe's incredulous eyes told him the little boy of a few seconds ago now had turned into a huge creature with a horrible face, long grappling arms and stump-sized feet that dragged the ground. The giant's ponderous hulk was about to crush the poor mule which weaved and staggered in painful distress.

After one look at the grotesque monster breathing down his neck, Rafe took off right over the mule's head, his feet running before he hit the ground. He fled screaming down the trail like a crazy man, slamming into trees and falling over obstacles in the darkness. When at last he came within sight of his own window, he yelled for his family to open the door. Headlong, he dashed inside and threw the bolt. And he didn't go back outside until the sun was an hour high next day.

No one believed Rafe's tale about the baby turning into a fearsome giant and crushing his mule. Many scoffed when they heard it and that hurt Rafe.

But weeks later, a young man from the other side of the Uwharries came courting into the area one Saturday night. He, too, traveled by muleback. Nightfall found him heading into Caesar's Swamp. A lighted lantern hung from his saddle and his hands strummed a battered guitar. He didn't notice the apprehension of his mule or the omens of the frogs and owls.

He was surprised when his mule stopped and he saw a bright baby on a log with his arms lifted, begging for a ride. He placed the boy close behind him on the mule's rump, just as Rafe had done. The mule had taken only a few steps before it was exhausted.

Two huge hands suddenly circled the young man and began thumping the guitar. He shrieked and attempted to vault over the mule's head but his feet became tangled in the stirrups and, trapped, he turned to face the horror of the creature behind him.

"His eyes was big as saucers!" he told people later. "Big gleams of light flashed out of them. I'm telling you, he was big as a haystack. He had my poor mule all crushed between his legs. Fire and smoke came snorting out of his mouth like a dragon. I could feel his breath scorching my face!"

Thereupon, the terrified man declared, he wrenched loose his foot and bulldozed a new path through that part of the swamp, his strapped guitar banging a medley behind him.

Another man soon met the spook of Caesar's Swamp.

He, too, picked up the baby, cradling him with one arm on his lap at the front of the saddle. And he swore that he saw the babe in his arms change right before his eyes into a gigantic monster with saucer eyes, feet and hands as large as stovewood boxes, and a hideous snout with nostrils erupting fire and smoke. The remainder of his life this man nursed a bruised thigh which he said the monster "sat on" until he could wrench free and fall off the horse.

Many years later a group of young daredevils, intrigued by a revival of interest in the swamp ghost, set about to tease the ghost and challenge it to reveal itself and the reason for its presence, or else get itself on back to ghostland and leave the swamp in peace.

They had taken into consideration the fact that the ghost hadn't actually harmed anyone, although it had broken down a few beasts of burden and given riders the shakes. The ghost had shown no viciousness toward humans. It just seemed to get a kick out of scaring the daylights out of people. So the young men planned to team up and go into the swamp in pairs to see what would happen.

Well after nightfall, two of them rode double into the swamp on the back of a plug mule, whose owner had donated it for the purpose. They left a group of impatient companions waiting around a bonfire. Another such group waited at another fire a mile away at the other side of the swamp. If anything happened and the boys got separated, they could make their way toward the fires.

The first two boys emerged from an uneventful trip through the swamp. Immediately two new boys mounted the bareback mule, grabbed the lantern, and started through. The sorties continued until they had exhausted the old mule. As their bravado increased, they left the mule to rest and half a dozen boys walked the trail without mishap. Emboldened now and scornful of the idea of a ghost, they lined up, lanterns glistening, and shouted ribald challenges into the shrouded thickets, daring the ghost to show himself. Nothing happened.

As the procession moved out of the swamp, two boys went back to get the old mule. As they returned, they spotted the luminous baby on a log, its arms lifted imploringly. Fear gripped them. They were alone now; the others had headed for home, confident that they had bested the ghost, if there had been such a thing. The boys kicked the tired mule closer. Surely this innocent little fellow couldn't be a ghost. The rear rider reached down and lifted the boy up, placing him between his companion and himself.

The moment the child was seated between them, the boys said later, the mule refused to budge. Instead, she began sinking to the ground as if flattened by a great weight. At the same time, the baby began to swell into a bulky mass threatening to engulf the boys.

The boy in front was shoved out onto the mule's neck and pitched headlong over its head. The boy on the rear felt himself pushed backward over the mule's rump until he went sprawling on the ground. Both stunned boys lay on the ground transfixed by what they saw.

They said the monster, by this time as big as two haystacks, danced a weird jig on the poor downed mule. He seemed to have two heads. When the monster's ugly snout opened, wicked teeth were exposed. Sometimes it belched flames and smoke. Its eyes, bigger than saucers, gleamed like a thousand cat eyes rolled into one. They remembered flying arms and legs and tails. The shifting, shapeless body lurched and cavorted in a macabre dance. Parts of the mysterious body flung themselves extremely far and twirled in derangement until sucked back into the mass. It did flipflops and somersaults. Little sound did it make as it trampled the mule and executed the crazy gymnastics.

Finally the boys crawled together and ran out of the swamp and into the remnants of the daredevil group, to whom they gasped out their frantic story. To humor them, the others turned up their lanterns and again penetrated the swamp. All they found was the old mule which seemed to have a deeper sway in its back.

For many years no one reported seeing the ghost of Caesar's Swamp again, although it was given ample opportunity and provocation to come out of its retirement and resume active ghosting again.

Then one night in late November, nearing the midnight hour, a group of coon hunters pushed their way through the swamp behind their dogs. They heard lusty cries of distress coming from a point in the depths of the swamp. A quick inventory showed one man missing. Guided by his cries, they found him beside a big log, his body wrapped in rough swamp vines which immobilized his arms and legs.

A straggler on the tail end of the hunting party, he had become drowsy from too much chill tonic and had fallen further behind than he realized. Abruptly, he was seized roughly from behind, lifted off his feet and his face smothered in something heavy and rough. He remembered being whizzed through the swamp thickets at an amazing speed. His struggles were ineffective against his unknown captor. He had no chance to resist or run before he felt the imprisoning vines covering his body.

The only thing he recalled clearly about his assailant was that his eyes were "brighter than cat eyes and bigger than saucers."

No one ever solved the mystery of the ghost of Caesar's Swamp, but a lot of people have speculated about it. Consider these theories: an actor perished in the quicksand of the swamp and his ghost craved an audience to watch his performance; an unwanted child was thrown into the swamp to die and its ghost kept coming back for vengeance; a mindless monster developed from the slime of the swamp.

Your own explanation may be as plausible as any advanced by the people of the Uwharries.

THE MUSICAL GHOST
OF ROCKY RIVER

Flaubert Greene, called "Bert" by his musician friends, arrived late to fill his slot in the small band for the evening concert and dance at Rocky River Springs Hotel in the southeastern fringe of the Uwharries. It was unusual for the fortyish, balding bachelor to be late for playing music at such an important gathering. Other members of the band noticed his flushed face and his collar soiled by perspiration. His eyes were brighter and he appeared elated and pleased, as well as impatient. A sheaf of scribbled-on paper bulged out of his coat pocket. Maybe they imagined it, but his big frame seemed to sway a bit contrary to the natural rhythm of the music.

Quickly he slipped in time and his banjo became a live thing in the hands of a master. It added instant lilt and harmony to the flow of music which had been limping prior to his arrival. Members of the audience smiled appreciatively. Some got up and danced.

Bert did feel heady this evening. He had something special. He hoped they called on him for a solo. Sometimes they did. Often the crowd clamored for his playing.

Later a break came in the playing and he took his glass of pink lemonade and found the band leader, Professor Ludwig. "I got a new one for tonight, if you need a solo, Professor. Brand new. No one's ever heard it before, because I just composed it late this afternoon down at the river. That's why I was late."

The scholarly old band director looked at him shrewdly for a moment and nodded.

When interest in dancing waned and the audience had had its fill of waltzes and fox trots, there came a personal request for a banjo tune by Bert. The other musicians faded and gave Bert the center of the brief riser stage at one end of the big room. A suspended gas lamp illuminated him and cast dashing shadows on the wall behind. Everyone in the room stopped still to watch and listen.

For the first time before any audience, Bert played this ballad he had written. The haunting melody had intense emotional impact which left the audience spellbound with dreamy faces. Women dabbed at their eyes and sniffed. All were visibly touched at the striking beauty of the tune. After he stopped, it was moments before anyone stirred from the spell of magic he had woven. Then someone asked him to play it again, and he played it a second time more beautifully than before.

The lyrics? They wanted to hear him sing the words to this spectacular number. Wouldn't he, please?

"There are no words, yet, I'm sorry," Bert told them. "I'm working on the words now, but they are not ready. Maybe later when I have time to work on them in solitude down by the river."

After the audience had gone, Bert tarried with the Professor and his two best friends in the band, Thurman, the guitarist, and Philas, the fiddler.

"It's working for me," he told them. "That spot down by the river. I can work better there. The music just comes to me there. I take my banjo and sit down near the water and it's so quiet and peaceful and still and inspiring. I can meditate and think and create. I can hear music all around me. I can write it down and fill it in and try it out on the banjo as I go. A lot of it is just fragments that I try to join together. Most of it is unfinished and I keep going back to learn the rest.

"Some of you boys have got to go with me and help me. At least one of you. The music will come to you, too. There's no reason it shouldn't. That way we can get it down faster. We'll go tomorrow afternoon."

The place by the river Bert referred to was a mile and a half by hiking trail south of the springs resort at the point where Alligator Branch empties into Rocky River. There the surface swirled and eddied over a suckhole with a depth that never had been probed.

Early white settlers in the area said Indians claimed alligators and shad from the Atlantic Ocean, 175 miles away, once infested the creek and that an Indian maiden had drowned herself here in heartbreak for her slain lover. There was talk that the Indians gave some of their departed brethren a headstart toward the Happy Hunting Grounds via the suckhole.

Young people from the resort often hiked down the scenic trail to the Indian Hole. But they were warned never to go in the water or even very near it because of the treacherous current that had taken at least three lives within memory of the community, the last one, some years back, being a young vacationer who had stumbled into the hole while playing his harmonica. Bodies of the victims, never found, were believed sucked into some faraway subterranean chamber.

Philas the fiddler came with Bert to the river late the next afternoon. It was his first trip to the lonely spot and he didn't like what he saw and felt, and he said so to Bert. But Bert didn't even hear him. Already, Bert was lost in his quest for that elusive music that came to him here.

With banjo swung from his neck and paper and pencil in his hand, he leaned against a tree, sat on a boulder tapering down to the water, propped his feet on the tangled driftwood clogging one side of the stream junction, and walked with measured paces amid the laurel and juniper bushes crowding one bank. Often he stopped, his head poised, his eyes studious, his ears cocked. His head bobbed and his body weaved in rhythm to music known only to him. He scribbled on his paper. Occasionally, he plunked out experimental notes on the banjo. His face glowed pleasure and satisfaction.

Philas experienced none of Bert's euphoria. Moreover, a look of apprehension came over his face now. He heard the murmuring, gurgling water on the rocks, the flurrying sound of the eddying current, the vines and foliage slithering and rustling in the breeze, birds twittering in the trees, a squirrel scolding the intruders from a distant limb. But music? No. He shook his head. As the sun lowered behind a ridge, the shadows deepened and Philas felt a sinister chill in the air.

Bert's behavior was not that of an inspired man creating a new song. Too mechanical. More like a man under a spell. More like a man copying down vagrant bits of music and waiting imploringly for more at the whim and mercy of some mysterious spell caster.

At last Philas had to shake Bert and pull him back toward the hotel.

"Why did you bother me?" Bert raged at his friend, wont to strike him. "Why? You ruined it. You broke the connection. Just when we were starting on the chorus. It was the best one yet. Now it's gone. I may never be able to get back on it. Why did you have to bother me? I got to have the rest of this new song and the missing parts of some others. I've just got to."

Philas talked to the Professor and the other bandsmen, emphasizing Bert's enchantment and his apparent insensibility to any danger. "We shouldn't let him go there alone," he said. "That place is creepy and ghosty to me. There's something evil there. I can feel it. It must have a spell on Bert."

Professor Ludwig decided it was a calculated risk worth taking, especially since Bert seemed so bent on going to the Indian Hole anyway. The new and original music Bert claimed to be getting from the hole found immediate favor with the important and mon-eyed families at the resort. Since they liked and appreciated this music, they would endorse it, tell other people about it back home, perhaps recommend him. This would vastly increase the popularity and renown of him and his band. It could mean off-season engagements this winter in some of the big cities, maybe even up north where some of the guests were from.

So, for the remainder of the season, the bandsmen took turns playing nursemaid to Bert as he soaked up new music from the musical ghost of Rocky River at the Indian Hole.

"Can't you hear it, can't you?" Bert raved at them. hoping vainly they, too, could receive and interpret this ghostly music which gripped him so mightily. He wanted them to help him capture it and record it and preserve it. "There it is! Listen, she's singing! Beautiful, oh, beautiful! Oh, Lord, let me get it all down this time!"

And he'd scribble feverishly on his paper. Then he walked around looking up, waiting expectantly for more of the ephemeral refrain apparently teasingly withheld and arbitrarily released in snatches. Then he'd practice the new notes on his banjo until more came.

Various members of the band accompanied Bert to the river. Some of them did hear fleeting snatches of song from a source they could not identify. It sounded like the voice of a young woman. Indistinct and fading, it was as frustrating as illegible handwriting. The harder they tried to listen and understand, the more unfathomable the singing became. One thing they agreed on – the voice was sad. It had a melancholy, dirgeful tone.

Professor Ludwig came and listened and marvelled, too. He agreed about the sadness in the voice. "Evidently the voice and the music are much clearer to Bert," he said. "Tell me, does he ever talk about the owner of the voice, or mention a girl's name?"

"Yeah, her name is Judy," Philas said. "I've heard him say that Judy is singing to him – that Judy is calling him. Why? Who's Judy?"

"He had a sweetheart by that name a long, long time ago," the Professor mused, a new realization dawning in his eyes.

As quickly as it could be shaped and practiced, this music was introduced by Bert and the band in the evening concert and dance sessions at the hotel before a select audience of refined and cultured people who came here from many faraway places to relax and partake of the health-giving waters of the healing springs. The new pieces were instant hits and successes. People raved and clamored over them. They played the band to exhaustion, particularly Bert. Many contacts were made by the Professor and a prosperous fall and winter season in northern nightspots illuminated the future.

But Bert began to crack under the pressure. He told them things were going too slowly and he was impatient to get more new music faster and to finish some of the fragmentary pieces he had collected. He would have to spend more time at the river.

Impulsively, he took to disappearing at odd times of the day and night and going to the Indian Hole before his friends were aware of his absence.

One day they arrived too late at the Indian Hole. They saw his tracks plainly in the earth sticky from a recent rain. Near the edge of the matted driftwood there fluttered beneath a splinter, a scrap of Bert's notepaper bearing some scribbled music. Out there the whirlpool swished and sloshed and kicked up dervishes of spray in unusual vigor.

As they watched the vortex dance around as if digesting its fresh victim, they heard the singing commence. The same indistinct voice...but with a difference. A difference so pronounced it caused startled looks and gasps from the men.

Now the feminine voice had lilt and laughter, a happy voice!

Professor Ludwig's eyes grew big and serious. His gray head jerked and a muscle twitched at the corner of his mouth. He motioned the members of the band closer. His voice came unsteadily.

"Her name was Judith Ann. She was a lovely thing. She had a voice that was classical and operatic. It would pretty nigh put the angels to shame. They were both in their twenties. He grew up in these parts and inherited some of his musical talent. She came here each summer with her folks from Delaware. We had a little band here even back then – just young Bert and myself and one or two other fill-ins. She would play the piano and sing by herself some evenings and sometimes she'd sing with our band. They fell in love. Completely. Totally. But her parents didn't like the idea and tried to discourage her. Bert couldn't give her up, but he couldn't have her either.

"One day they walked here to the Indian Hole. Something happened. I don't know what. Bert said she slipped and fell in the water. Her folks claimed he threw her in. She may have jumped in by herself. They never found the body and the law couldn't do anything with him. Bert wandered off and rambled for years, stopping and playing his banjo here and there over the country. He'd write me once every year or so. Last spring he wrote and said make room for him in the band this season because he was returning home – that something was pulling him back. Well...the power a woman has over a man. Even in death. Even after all these years. I hope they're together now and happy."

Little of Bert's music survived. Maybe a few chords, a few bars, lines and words bob up here and there. A vacationing music teacher at the hotel wrote down the music of several of Bert's special numbers, but whenever she or anyone tried to play them something happened and they never came out right. Time gradually erased even these.

Rocky River Springs faded as a resort many decades ago when

the automobile came into vogue. Forest growth has long since obscured the trail down Alligator Branch. Seldom does anyone ever visit the Indian Hole, by which the river flows wild and lonely. But the belief persists that any person with an ear for music, particularly a musically talented person with a flair for originality, can come into the quietness of this spot and soon hear the sound of music. This hauntingly beautiful music easily can be identified as faint but gay singing and fragments from the piano and banjo – the latter distinctly in the style and arrangement of that once played by Flaubert Greene.

BLUEBEARD
OF THE UWHARRIES

A knitting needle typical of those used by the early settlers in the Uwharries as well as elsewhere along the eastern seaboard, was a tiny round shaft of steel, springy, and tapered to a point on either end. No larger than the lead in an ordinary wooden pencil, it measured about eight or nine inches in length. A set of four such needles customarily were used in knitting woolen sox and stockings, the prime products of the knitting needles of that day. Constant use in the nimble fingers of the women of the household kept the needles shiny and bright and gleaming.

It is highly possible that there exists in some North Carolina home today one such needle used by Bluebeard of the Uwharries to murder his seven wives....

...And that his ghost is still searching for this needle. It may be a single needle now or it may be one of a set, treasured as a family heirloom, as a memento of the past, and used and displayed only at the vagaries of sentiment. It will be tarnished now from decades of idleness. Unless good care has been taken of it, the tiny rod of metal will be flecked with spots of corrosion, reminiscent of splotches of blood.

Regardless of who possesses this particular knitting needle now – and there is little to aid the layman in distinguishing this grisly specimen from any other knitting needle of the period – it is most unlikely that they know anything at all of its buckets-of-blood past.

Unlike the swashbuckling Bluebeard of the fairy tales who married and murdered six wives and was about to kill the seventh when he, himself, was slain, the Uwharrie Bluebeard had no outstanding physical characteristics, being an average farming man in size and appearance. Of a meek and unpretentious temperament, he assumed a quiet detachment and preoccupation which insulated him and his household from most of the social intercourse of the day. This withdrawal from community activities became more noticeable as the list of his wives lengthened.

Regardless of his peculiar social habits, no one in the Uwharrie settlement could have imagined this outwardly mild farmer capable of the atrocities which he later admitted had been performed by his hand.

Apparently he had no children or other family members occupying his big two-story log farmhouse, just himself and his succession of wives.

His first wife, the one with whom he lived the longest, became adept at knitting. Since she had no young ones of her own, she knitted stockings and gave them to the children of the community. Her husband became fascinated by the four shiny knitting tools and he sat by the hour and watched her manipulate them. When she tired of knitting and went to bed, he sometimes sat before the fireplace and fondled the four needles until late at night.

No one suspected anything amiss when Bluebeard's first wife and later his second, died suddenly. Women of the community gathered and prepared the bodies for burial in the family plot on the homestead. To those visiting in the home and attending the burying, Bluebeard appeared normally crushed about the deaths. He even shed a few tears as he looked into the pine boxes for the last time before they were closed and lowered forever into the earth.

By the time the third and fourth of the Bluebeard wives were dead and buried under similar circumstances, people began to wonder and talk surreptitiously to their neighbors of the strange series of deaths at the Bluebeard home.

By the time wives number five and six had been buried in the expanding graveyard near the big log house, people were sure it could no longer be mere coincidence that Bluebeard's wives kept dying in such regular sequence and under such mysterious circumstances. Many questions were asked openly now and vile epithets were muttered as the name of the man who lived in the big house by the growing graveyard was mentioned. But no one knew anything for certain. No one could prove a thing on him. Growing older now, he became a figure of odd and peculiar significance and parents used his name to frighten their children into obedience.

At each wake and burying he appeared broken. During the wake, while his currently dead wife lay a corpse in the home, people could see him make repeated trips to the basket which held the knitting last done by his beloved's hand. While he caressed the unfinished knitted garment and fondled the gleaming knitting needles, a few tears on his cheeks made his face appear to contort in anguish.

Within a few months after the death of each of his wives, Bluebeard would hitch up his horse to his buggy, drive away and be gone for days, sometimes weeks. When he came back, he had a new wife with him. Folks said he went clean out of the county, or across several counties, where no one had ever heard of him, there to woo and win a new wife.

And every time Bluebeard arrived back home with a new wife, the people of the community shook their heads and looked sad. The womenfolks said: "The poor, poor soul. I grieve for her so."

But their concern for the new wife did not lead them to try to visit her and warn her about the dark whispers concerning her husband or about the unaccountable deaths of his previous wives. Nor did any of the new wives, after a futile attempt or two, try to visit or communicate with the neighboring women. People wondered what Bluebeard told his new wives when they asked about that row of neat graves out at the edge of the yard.

Apparently all his wives either already knew how to knit or were taught by him soon after their arrival. People passing on the road could see the current Mrs. Bluebeard sitting outside the house on sunny days with the knitting needles flashing in her lap. Never was her husband far away. Sitting watching his wife knit was his favorite pastime.

At the demise of wife number seven a peculiar thing happened. A man witnessed Bluebeard in the very act of killing his wife.

It was the custom in those days for vagabond peddlers to stop and seek lodging and meals wherever nighttime or mealtime caught them on the country roads. Such a peddler stopped at the Bluebeard home at dusk one evening and for some strange reason, an uncharacteristic action for the head of the domicile, the peddler was accepted for the night. After a nourishing supper, prepared and served by the wife, and a session of spotty conversation before the bright fireplace, the peddler was shown to his upstairs room. As he left, he saw the man's wife busily knitting in her chair near the fireplace.

A scraping noise awoke the peddler later in the night. He crept to the door, opened it and went down the twisting stairs where he could peek out into the big room. There sat Bluebeard polishing and sharpening one of the knitting needles on a whetstone. Absorbed in his task, Bluebeard paused occasionally to inspect the shiny needle close to the glowing lamp globe and to test its point with his finger.

As he went back to his room, the peddler thought: Why was it necessary to sharpen the point of a knitting needle? Didn't normal use keep the needle sharp enough and shiny enough? And, anyway, wasn't that a job for the woman instead of the man?

Still later in the night, the peddler awoke again as he heard movement in the room below him. A thin shaft of light, coming through a knothole in the floor near his bed, drew his attention. He got out of bed and dropped down on the floor and looked through the hole.

What he saw in the next few minutes engraved a picture on his mind that never would be erased.

In the room below, Bluebeard set the lamp on the table by the bed where his wife lay sleeping. Light from the lamp gleamed off the slender knitting needle in his hands. He drew back the bed covers and before the woman came fully to her senses, her husband jerked her nightgown down around her waist where it ensnared her arms and hands. The knitting needle in his hands descended slowly toward the woman's naked breast.

She screamed once. "Oh, Lord," she moaned pitiably. She tried to scream again. After a few minutes of faint struggling she lay quiet and still and lifeless on the bed.

Bluebeard remained around the bed for a few minutes while the peddler, froze to the knothole with fear, watched from above. With a rag, he wiped clean the knitting needle. Every few minutes, he wiped blood from the breast of the still body of his wife on the bed until the blood came no more. Satisfied that the bleeding had stopped, he replaced her nightgown, straightened the bed covers, took the lamp, and left the room in darkness.

Knowing he would be next, the peddler stood trembling by the door ready to attempt a dash for freedom when Bluebeard and his needle appeared. But no one approached his door. After an hour or two he sat down, fully clothed, on the bed with a quilt around him and dozed numbly, his mind awhirl at the horror of what he had seen in that dark room beneath him.

At dawn, he heard heavy feet bounding up the stairs. His room door jerked open and there stood Bluebeard, his gray hair awry, an expression of shock on his ashen face.

"My wife's dead!" he said to the cowering peddler in a shrill tone of pretended anguish. "I found her dead in the bed downstairs. Somebody's got to come and help me fix her. You get up and go tell some of the neighbors around here she's dead and to come and help me get her fixed up."

The peddler hastily complied, immensely relieved to escape the man's house.

His pounding at the first house brought to the door a half-dressed man followed by a woman in a nightcap. Once inside, he blurted out his story, telling them he firmly believed Bluebeard killed his wife with the knitting needle. The man and woman nodded in agreement. They routed two half-grown sons out of bed and sent them scurrying out to carry the news to other households in the community. Soon, a dozen or so men and women, the peddler in their midst, arrived at the home of the dead woman and were met by Bluebeard.

He led them inside and stood by the bed wringing his hands as they came up to look at the dead woman. One of the men addressed the women. "Us men will go outside the door here and wait. You womenfolks look that dead woman over real close. See if you can find any hole or wound that might have caused her death."

While the women went to work, the men backed outside into the larger room. Bluebeard cowered in the midst, surrounded by men determined to confront him at last with the suspicions and accusations they had harbored for many years.

The peddler kept mumbling dazedly: "I seen him do it."

A woman came out and reported. Yes, there was a tiny blue hole under the woman's left breast which could have been made by a knitting needle.

The men turned toward Bluebeard, backed against the wall now. A long barreled gun appeared in one man's hands, its muzzle swinging to cover Bluebeard. Another man grabbed up a club-sized stick of firewood from beside the fireplace. Another man began unwinding a coil of rope and fashioning a noose in the end.

"Did you kill her?" one asked.

Bluebeard broke then. His head jerked. His eyes brightened queerly and refused to focus on anyone. But he grinned a ghastly smile as he said: "Yes, I killed her. "

"With the knitting needle?"

He nodded.

"And how about your other wives?"

Bluebeard's glittering eyes looked far away. But his face had turned wrinkled and hideous. His mouth was half smile, half snarl.

"Yeah, I killed them. Killed them all. All with the same knitting needle. All the same way."

"But how could you. I mean, why did you?" the stunned questioner asked.

"I couldn't stop," Bluebeard said. "Not after the first two. I just couldn't stop it."

So shocked were they by the enormity of this revelation, the men momentarily relaxed their vigilance. Bluebeard sidled over to the edge of the fireplace. His hand reached up and removed something from the top edge of a thin wooden strip fastened over the crack between the logs. He fumbled at his shirt front. With a gasp of pain he slumped to his knees, then fell heavily on his face to the floor. His body shuddered once or twice and remained still.

Directly, they turned him over and found that the deliberate fall to the floor had finished ramming a tiny silver rod of metal through his heart, the final beats of which had pumped out enough blood to stain the floor around where he lay.

Two new graves were added to the row outside the big log house, Bluebeard's, on the end, dominating even in death the graves of the seven women he murdered by his own admittance.

They say some intrepid soul removed the knitting needle from Bluebeard's heart before the burying.

Speculation was that Bluebeard, afflicted with a maniacal compulsion to thrust his knitting needle into the quivering heart of a living woman, would have made way with a dozen women or more had not the peddler chanced to witness the seventh killing and expose him. Gradually, other women who had participated in the preparation of the dead wives for burial at one time or another, reported seeing a similar tiny dark hole around the breast of the dead women. Conjured up in the minds of these people was the image of a devilishly bloodthirsty man who enjoyed toying with his woman until the novelty of a new wife wore off, whereupon he manifested his boredom and satisfied his cravings by shoving his trusty knitting needle through her terrified and palpitating heart, a morbid act of addiction which he probably could not resist. This is the image of him handed down in Uwharrie folklore. The wives of Bluebeard are thought of as timid, spiritless women, broken to his will, imprisoned in the home, made dour, silent, and brooding under the nerve-wracking suspense they must have endured as they began to realize bit by bit the fate that awaited them at the whims of a madman.

Time and decades gradually obliterated the old log house and a young forest rose around it, hiding the ruins of the house and the row of graves from view.

While the house remained livable, several families and people lived there temporarily. Among them were Aunt Jancie and her old maid daughter, Mary, who occupied the house, rent-free, while they picked cotton for nearby farmers. Both feeble and senile, they reported hearing and seeing the ghosts of Bluebeard and his wives all around the place.

Almost every night they heard someone walk heavily up on the porch, wipe off his feet on the sack and dump what sounded like an armful of firewood in the wood box on the porch. Investigation into these and other noises proved nothing.

These women and other occupants said they could come into the big room, day or night, and sometimes see the shape of a woman busily knitting in a chair near the fireplace, a woman with a sad face who always vanished when they moved near. Or they could see the shape of a man playing with some knitting needles which he held up close to his face. Some were frightened to hear the painful plea "Oh, Lord!" come from within the dark depths of the old house in the middle of the night. Nighttime hunters and travelers in the vicinity told of seeing white shapes resembling women knitting rise up out of the ground and flitter away into the starlit sky. Mysterious deaths of wild and domestic animals, with puncture wounds in their bodies, were attributed to Bluebeard's ghost and his still lethal needle.

Who kept the knitting needle pulled from Bluebeard's murderous heart – the needle which had taken eight human lives – is not remembered. However, it is believed to have changed hands many times since then. There are those who say Bluebeard's ghost, confused by these transactions, prowls nightly among the homes in and around the Uwharries looking for its knitting needle. If you have such a needle and value it, they advise you to keep it under lock and key, or else secreted in an inaccessible hiding place.

On the other hand, if you think the needle you possess could be the authentic Bluebeard one, it might be a good idea to leave it conspicuously placed outside your house at night, for if the fondling hands of Bluebeard's ghost are ever reunited with that long lost needle, it could be that the first thing the ghost will seek is a quivering heart to puncture.

THE GHOST
OF PRETTY SALLY STEED

Satiated from a Saturday night of carousing at Big Lick, Alph Perry rode his mare, Bertie, back home along the wagon road by the old Dock Dunn cotton gin. Tired and drowsy, he gripped the saddle horn and gave Bertie a free rein because she knew where to go.

As the fast walking mare passed the old gin, a white shape flashed out of the decrepit structure and leaped up on the mare behind the rider.

Bertie came alive with a snort, a whinny of alarm and lunged off at a fast gallop. Alph might have been thrown had he not wakened sufficiently to grab leather and hang on. He sensed something behind him and twisted to peer over his shoulder.

"It was her – just as real and purty as life!" he told people afterward. "That long hair and that peachy face and them fancy riding clothes and that nice shape. I know it was her. Sally Steed. Purty Sally Steed. I know she was a ghost 'cause I could see right on through her!"

It took Alph a mile to get the wildly galloping Bertie reined in. By that time the ghost of Sally Steed had vanished.

"She didn't speak or do nothing," Alph reflected. "Just rode behind the saddle a ways. Might've clung to me a little. Seems like she kicked old Bertie in the ribs and slapped her rump to speed her up. Still a horsewoman."

Before her untimely death a few years earlier, Sally Steed had been a young woman who loved to ride horses, any horse with spirit and sense. Her well-to-do father, a farmer and gin operator, was prosperous enough to indulge Sally, his only child, in her passion for horses. She did well. Her shrewd trading and breeding attracted horse fanciers from distant places, as well as other equestrians who came to ride and race with her on weekends and festive occasions.

The long level stretch of road by the old gin became a favorite riding place to try out new animals and to time them against each other. Crowds gathered on Saturday and Sunday afternoons to watch some of the very best horseflesh in the area perform. Sally stayed right in the middle of it all. Young and immensely pleasing to the eye, she attracted many young men who came courting, only to be spurned by the effervescent Sally who said horses were more important to her than men. She was happy only with a good horse under her.

Some days didn't have enough daylight in them to satisfy Sally's riding urge, so she spent the early evening hours riding in the light of the stars and moon, to train her mounts to run and jump and prance. Often she rode alone.

Occasionally her parents came to watch. Infrequently, a brash young horseman, more interested in Sally than horses, came to ride with her. Though none of them succeeded, the young swains figured they had a better chance of wooing Sally alone in the moonlight. But most always the horses got in the way.

The accident occurred near the end of one such nocturnal solo riding session. Sally's sprinting mount shied, broke his stride, fell and rolled on top of her with crushing force. She lay unconscious, broken, bruised and bleeding for an hour before her parents came looking and found her. They carried her home and tenants fetched old Doc Anderson who examined her and shook his head.

"Back's crushed all up. One leg busted. One wrist splintered to pieces. Neck almost snapped. Terrible lick on her head. No telling what damage inside. She'll never ride again, probably never stand. And she'll be blind, too. Lucky if she lives."

She did live for a while. Long enough to come to her senses, realize her hopeless condition, fail to adjust, and wallow in self pity. Despair, heartbreak, bitterness and inconsolable grief were burdens her broken body and spirit could not withstand.

Sally Steed died and they buried her in the family plot up the slope from the road where she could keep eternal vigil on her favorite riding place.

"She grieved herself to death," said one neighbor who knew Sally well. "Knowing she could never ride again was death already. She was blind and paralyzed, but she got so she could talk a little. Claimed something strange rose out of the bushes and spooked her horse, the same horse she had been riding and working with for two hours. It must have been strange and unusual and sudden, because she was wise to the ways of all horses. That fall broke up the horse, too, and it had to be shot."

For two or three years people encountered nothing unusual as they used the road freely. Riders still came to try out their mounts and occasionally there were races when owners, local and visiting, claimed horseflesh of unrivaled excellence. But these events were as nothing compared to the flamboyant days when Sally glamorized the gatherings.

Promoting these events and gradually assuming a leading role as horseman and showman of promise was Reath Haughter, a local young man Sally's age who had been, in community opinion, the one most likely to win and woo her hand if such was possible. A striking specimen of masculinity in his fancy riding togs, Reath rode well and he advocated riding for everyone, suggesting that young horse-backers of the area carry on the riding tradition in honor of Sally Steed, who, perhaps, was proudly watching from where she slept on the hillside.

Then Alph Perry had his experience here. The news spread fast that perhaps Sally was riding again after all. Subsequent encounters with the ghost confirmed it. Use of the road declined, especially at night when most of the ghostly riding occurred.

Mostly it was single horseback riders the ghost joined for a brief ride along the gin road. Invariably, the riders and animals panicked and in the melee, the riders could give no coherent account of just what took place. No one ever thought it was the lack of horsemanship expertise which caused the horse to bolt when the ghost boarded, but simply the animal's and the rider's instinctive reaction of hysteria to the abrupt appearance of the supernatural. As more and more riders claimed to have been the unwilling host to the ghost of

Sally Steed for a brief moonlight sojourn behind the saddle along the gin road, a pattern of sorts began to emerge from their animated descriptions of the few dramatic moments.

The ghost leaped aboard anywhere along the mile or so stretch of road by the gin place, but seldom rode beyond it. No rider knew when she got off, since she just vanished. Most claimed she clutched them on the arms and around the middle and that they could feel her hands on their faces. They all grunted and cried in surprise and some asked what she wanted, but the ghost never made any response. Neither did she try to control the horse. She just rode for a ways and hopped off or vanished.

Strangely, no rider ever experienced the ghost of Sally Steed twice. Always it was a different rider who found her riding double with him. Though the earlier victims used the road normally afterward, there was never a repeat performance with the same rider.

This caused some speculation. Was it a particular horse or a particular rider, or both, the ghost sought? Or was it because death just couldn't be allowed to stand in the way of one who loved riding as much as Sally had?

It got to be something of a game with the young men of the area. Boys who felt they were ready to prove their manhood did so by a solo ride at night on the gin road and a frightening experience with the ghost of Sally Steed. And then they crowed about it. Newcomers came often enough to keep the ghost in trim riding form.

Reath Haughter didn't ride horseback in the area anymore after the ghost of Sally became active there. "I loved her so much I couldn't bear going back there now and seeing her as a ghost," he confided to a close friend one day. A prosperous trader and businessman now, he lived alone in his home on the slope of Big Lick Mountain. Outside of making more money, his only interest was his whiskey and his fireside where he sat alone each night pathetically torturing himself over his unrealized love for Sally Steed.

Several of Reath's contemporaries, all of whom had greatly admired, if not secretly loved, Sally, discussed Reath and his plight one day. "It's not good for him to sit up there in that fine house alone every night grieving himself to death," said Reaves Cannady, his closest comrade since boyhood. "We got to do something to perk him up and get some new life into him."

Each of them had experienced the ghost of Sally Steed and they knew she held no malice. Maybe that's what Reath needed. Get him down here and send him through and let him meet the harmless ghost. Maybe that would snap him out of his despair and convince him that Sally was still happily doing what she liked best, riding horses. Why shouldn't he accept that she was happy, stop moping around and develop some new interests?

New Year's Day was approaching. They decided to build a bonfire beside the gin road, invite a few other friends, including some young women, and sing and eat and talk around the fire to welcome in the new year. Surely Reath would respond to an invitation to participate.

After supper on New Year's Eve, one of the men went to get Reath in a buggy. He came only reluctantly, brought more by the enticement of a good drink of five-year-old brandy than by the festivity. When he arrived and realized the location, he acted jittery and kept looking apprehensively into the darkness. However, the brandy, the fire, the fellowship and the tinkling laughter of the women, loosened him some and he joined halfheartedly in their singing and banter.

Reaves Cannady wanted Reath to try out a new saddle and determine if he had made a good trade for it. He assisted Reath into the saddle and pointed out special features on it.

"While you're mounted, you might as well try it out in a gallop down the road and back," he said, signalling another man ready with a doubled leather strap who rapped the horse stingingly on the rump, sending it snorting off at a furious gallop down the gin road.

Realizing what was happening, Reath's shrill voice drifted back: "No, don't. I can't ride here. Let me tell you something. It won't do. Don't..." But the horse, smarting from the lash, had some running to get out of his system and wasn't listening to any pleas. Horse and rider vanished into the black corridor between the trees.

"Jim's waiting at the other end to be sure he's all right when he gets down there," Reaves said.

But he didn't get that far. They heard the noise of the horse falling and tumbling. They heard the man's sharp cry of fear followed by groans of agony. Telling the girls to wait by the fire, the men took lanterns and firebrands and rushed to the scene.

Reath Haughter lay twisted on his back, broken, crushed, lacerated and limp as a rag doll. His eyes stretched wide with fear. His blood spattered moustache quivered as his voice struggled to survive.

"It was her. She leaped on behind me. She felt my face, then caused the horse to fall and roll over on top of me. Just like I did to her that night. Yeah, I did it. I wanted to marry her, but she wouldn't even notice me. I was mad at her and wanted to slow her down some. I got me a straw dummy and a white sheet and hid in the bushes and spooked her horse when it passed. Then I run away. But I never meant to kill her. I loved her. I wanted..."

Coughing more blood, Reath Haughter died there in a patch of moonlight on the rain-washed gravel of the Dock Dunn Gin Road.

A noise a little ways further down the road caused the shocked men to stand and look. There was the horse Reath had ridden, apparently unhurt, ambling about and rubbing its forelegs.

Then the slim white shape of a woman appeared beside it, vaulted into the saddle and grabbed up the reins. Heels dug into the animal's sides. A hand slashed toward his rump. The horse lunged into a fast gallop down the road with the lithe figure leaning easily forward like an expert horsewoman.

"We'll find the horse down at the other end," Reaves Cannady predicted. "That was Sally Steed. She couldn't resist taking one last ride now that she's accomplished her purpose."

THE GHOSTS
OF THE BOILED BODIES

Ghosts used to sit on the front porch and talk with Uncle Abraham Shadd at his two-story home on the banks of Haw Branch near the foot of Lick Mountain. People passing actually saw the white figures of the ghosts occupying the chair beside Abe's rocker. However, when they turned in off the road to come on up close to the house, they always found the chair vacant. But, often, they saw tears on Abe's cheeks and a faraway look of nostalgia in his eyes and they knew that Abe and one of his ghost friends had just been talking about the old days. Sometimes on these occasions they found it difficult to arouse old Abe and make him notice his earthly visitors.

If questioned about the reality and identity of the white figure occupying the chair moments before, Uncle Abe shrugged it away with a snaggle-toothed grin and commented: "Jest one of my friends from back in the old days." Or else, he'd feign ear trouble and couldn't hear a thing.

One curious eavesdropper concealed himself beside the porch in the cool of the evening and reported the following conversation between Abe and the ghost, though it was the ghost who did most of the talking:

"You remember old man Petticord Brothers, don't you, Abe? Well, he's up at Richmond. They rattle his bones around in the classroom every day. Of course, you remember little Joy Bell with the long nose? The daughter of Flave and Hassie Davis? She's in the pediatrics department at the School of Medicine at the University of Michigan. And old Samp Bogan who had six fingers on each hand and a big knob of bone sticking out of each leg? The orthopedists at Duke wanted him to study. Old Samp has been shifted around a good deal."

Uncle Abe just grunted and nodded, the eavesdropper said, and once in awhile inquired about the whereabouts of some mutual friend, long deceased, and the ghost would tell him.

The names mentioned by the ghost rang bells in the community. "Why them folks has been dead for thirty or forty years or longer," an oldster said. "But they's plenty of folks around here that remembers 'em."

Someone asked the eavesdropper, a man in his fifties, if he had ever before heard the voice of the ghost. "You may think I'm crazy as hell," he said. "And I know he died back when I was a kid, but it sounded just like the voice of old Preacher Dandy Lucas."

No one much believed the eavesdropper, but a group of men decided to go ask Uncle Abe about it.

"Yep, that's right, it was Dandy," Uncle Abe said after he understood their question. They reminded him that Preacher Dandy had been dead 30 or 40 years. "Oh, he still comes back to see me now and then," Abe responded matter-of-factly, as if he also could have told them that other of his long departed former friends "came back" to see him now and then, too, which they wouldn't have believed any more than they believed him now. Still they marveled at the unexplained white figures which continued to occupy the guest chair on the front porch and chat with Abe in the cool of the evenings.

The perplexity of the people increased manyfold in the next year or so as old Abe, feeling that his end was near, delighted in telling bizarre tales to anyone who had the patience to stop and listen. But by this time most people ridiculed old Abe and were disinclined to put much credence in his rambling tales. Some questioned his mental stability. However, there was just enough fact in his tales to lodge doubt in many a mind.

In his younger days, Abe worked for and lived with two pioneer doctors of the Haw Bridge area, who worked together and made their headquarters in a large, two-story, renovated farmhouse a couple miles from the little community. Whether they were reputable medical doctors, or quacks, no one remembers. Anyway, their services were extensively used throughout the territory.

Abe's job was to tend to their buggy horses, keep their wagons in repair, distill a little medicinal whiskey from time to time, cultivate a garden which included special vegetables and fruits, roam the woods for certain wild herbs, and a miscellany of other handyman tasks. He even did the cooking and household chores since they allowed no female housekeeper or anyone else to remain in the house longer than necessary. Abe also made trips for the doctors to the nearest railroad station to bring supplies and to ship various cargoes which went away from the house.

But these were activities of which most people were aware. What they didn't know, probably did not even suspect, were the shadowy, bone-chilling goings-on which old Abe gradually began to tell about in his old age, a good quarter of a century after his two elderly doctor friends had packed up and left the country, telling him they wouldn't be surprised if they didn't eventually wind up in Florida to enjoy the sunshine for the rest of their days.

As a reward for his long service to them, the doctors bequeathed Abe the farmhouse and all their possessions which they could not ship ahead or take with them. People wondered if this generous act didn't have much to do with keeping Abe's lips effectively sealed until long after his benefactors were gone.

According to Abe, doctoring was only a sideline with the two doctor partners. Their main objective was wholesale grave robbing, defleshing the corpses, and shipping their processed skeletons for distribution to other doctors, medical centers, and medical schools for purposes of study. And, though it's ghastly to contemplate, the question arises that since their main interest lay in dead bodies rather than live ones, if this interest did not influence their dealings with their monopoly of patients within a radius of a dozen miles or so.

Many was the night, old Abe said, that he and one or both the doctors had gone to a lonely graveyard at midnight and shoveled away the loose earth from a fresh grave. After they removed the pine box containing the corpse, they dropped in several short lengths of logs prepared for this purpose, to fill the space. Then they raked the earth back in the hole, rearranged the flowers on top, and no one ever became the wiser.

The corpse, still intact in the box, was hauled back to the two-story house on Haw Branch for processing in the doctors' secret workshop. In a special metal vat over a stone fireplace, they boiled the body in hot liquids until the flesh shredded away and left a perfect skeleton. After a little aging and preserving treatment, the skeleton was packed in its original casket and shipped. Labels on such boxes identified the contents as medical supplies. Despite the heavy padding which protected the fragile skeletons, none of the boxes was heavy enough to arouse suspicions.

"My boss says it's cheaper to buy these body boxes to use for his herbs than it is to make his own," Abe used to tell the railroad clerks, none of whom ever questioned the contents.

Many complications and dramatic crises arose in the work from time to time, according to Abe, any one of which could have doomed the doctors' lucrative practice.

Once an out-patient recovered more quickly than the doctors intended. The recuperated young man began exploring the old house and accidentally stumbled into a small room filled with skeletons of different sizes hanging by wires from the ceiling. He went running through the house screaming about seeing a roomful of ghosts.

Another time a family decided it wanted to exhume the body of a loved one recently departed for some reason. This grave had been robbed by Abe and the doctors only a few hours after the interment and the skeleton of that body was hanging in the aging room. The doctors spent a few anxious days until one of them visited the family and volunteered the advice that to unearth the body might be foolhardy, since such graves had been known to emit a fatal poisonous gas when tampered with. He advised them to wait at least a few years before exhuming.

Occasionally when the pickings were slim, the doctors journeyed miles away to graveyards to bring bodies back for processing. On these jaunts, the doctors would leave on horseback when they had finished loading the body, leaving Abe to drive back alone in the wagon with the illicit cargo disguised under loose straw. Once a sleepy Abe drove up with an empty wagon. The doctors were horrified. Dawn hung imminently in the eastern sky. They had to find the box and its telltale cargo and conceal it before some early traveler made a gruesome discovery which would be a bombshell in the community.

Miraculously, they found it. One of the doctors galloped back over the trail on horseback and found the box, battered by its fall, and dragged it into the bushes to await Abe and the wagon. In the clear light of dawn, they reloaded the box and the doctor sat on it all the way back to prevent further mishap.

For years Abe and the two doctors continued their grave robbing, body boiling, and skeleton shipping. In the latter years of their business, they became quite brazen about it.

Abe said the two doctors visited most of the grave diggers and pointed out how unnecessary it was to dig deep graves when shallow graves would do just as well. Their professional suggestion was a grave covered only by two feet of soil at most. In subsequent grave-robbings this saved the trio a lot of labor.

They were able to steal some bodies before they reached the graveyard.

The doctors successfully sold the people of the community on the idea of letting them take the casket and body by their workshop to apply a "preserving powder" before carrying it on to the grave. This magic chemical, naturally, could only be applied minutes before burial in order to work effectively in retarding immediate decay. However, once inside the privacy of the workshop, the body was removed from the casket and hidden. Then bulky ballast of equal weight was wedged into place in the casket, the lid fastened securely, and the box taken on to the cemetery and buried.

While he was an obedient worker who earned good wages, Abe nevertheless had scruples. He knew it was wrong to desecrate the dead this way and his intrinsic honesty motivated him to try to make amends. Sometimes he went off by himself and fell on his knees and asked his Lord to forgive him for his part in the business.

Since the doctors let Abe do most of the heavy work, the body lugging and boiling and the dumping of the residue, the big man had opportunity to show his commiseration for the dead people. He handled the bodies tenderly and lovingly, especially those of his friends and the people with whom he was acquainted. He was careful not to bump them or jar them as he undressed the bodies and placed them in the vat. Always, he talked to them soothingly as if they could hear his voice, and he comforted them, even as the flesh shredded from their bones in the hot liquids of the vat. Abe continued to be their friend and to grieve for them as he dumped the buckets of flesh in the creek and as he painted the skeletons with a preserving solution and hung them in the aging room to cure under the supervision of the doctors. He became so attached to some of the skeletons, like his favorite old Preacher Dandy Lucas, that he wept when the time came to recommit the bones to the box for shipment.

Incredible as it seems, no one ever caught onto this business, according to Abe, and the doctors departed the community as respected men with many a tearful farewell being said over their retiring and leaving. One of their last requests was for the community to "Look out" for old Abe, their trusted associate and handyman for so many long years.

And the community did so. The women fussed over him and the farmers and businessmen favored him with odd jobs enough to keep him occupied, though their jobs were much milder than those to which he had been accustomed.

Folks remembered that in his siege of sickness which heralded the end, Abe was heard to say, "Them poor dead faces is all around me" and to wail in terror for someone to "Get them flying things away from me." But he didn't suffer much. He just grew steadily worse and died within a few days.

No one robbed the grave of Abraham Shadd. At least nothing mortal, that is.

Tales of ghosts precipitated by Abe's stories still linger among the people around the Lick Mountain vicinity. One is that back in the good old days, huge catfish, fattened by years of feeding off the cooked human flesh dumped into Haw Branch, could be caught occasionally by fisherman along the stream – and that "ghost" descendants of these huge fish can still be pulled to the surface of the water by fishermen but never landed.

All sorts of weird noises and sights are reported around the place where the doctors' old house once stood on Haw Branch. Most of these spooks are thought to be the ghosts of the victims of the grave robbing coming back to look for their flesh so ignominiously stripped from their bodies.

Other people contend, however, that credit for the frightening tales about the flying gargoyles divebombing people and squawking in guttural human voices should go to the moonshiners who spread these calculated rumors to discourage visitors who might interfere with their illegal operations in the Haw Branch area.

Even today when you ride through the Haw Branch section of the Uwharries in the cool of the evening, folks claim you can see one or two white human-like shapes around a certain old homeplace and a certain old graveyard. They say it's the ghost of Preacher Dandy Lucas coming to sit with Abraham Shadd to chat with him about the old days.

THE GHOST
WITH THE DIRTY CLOTHES

A preacher in the Uwharries used to tell from his pulpit this tale of an experience he had one spring night in the days when automobiles were still a novelty in these hills.

Wrestling his battered touring car along an unimproved road somewhere between the Yadkin River and Troy in the evening twilight, the preacher saw an old woman standing at the roadside. On her head she balanced a bulky bundle – a sheet with the corners tied together and filled with something lumpy and heavy enough to make her stoop.

The preacher stopped abreast of the woman. Her eyes regarded him without expression. Wrinkles had turned the skin of her face into a map of many features. Her dress, soiled and shapeless, almost dragged the ground. A stained bonnet all but hid the snow of her hair.

Tipping his hat and smiling a greeting, the preacher got down from his car. "May I help you carry that heavy load, sister?" he offered. "I'll be glad to have you ride with me as far down the road as you're going." Under her burden, the old woman nodded acceptance. He helped her deposit the bundle on the back seat of the car. It contained soiled clothing, he noticed, and he decided she must be a washwoman taking the clothes for laundering.

The ancient one moved slowly as the preacher helped her onto the front seat and closed the car door. They bounced on down the road. Stars peeked out and the sky held promise of an early moonrise. Over the steady chick-a-lacking of the engine came the calling of night birds and the croaking of frogs. The night breeze was pleasant. The preacher felt talkative.

But he found his aged companion a strange and silent passenger. She responded to his attempts at conversation with grunts and meaningless jerks of the head. Perhaps she was deaf, he thought. Many aged people were. When she glanced at him her eyes were uncommunicative.

Soon he began to wonder how far she was going. He asked where she wanted to get out. She ignored him. Repeatedly he asked her, finally shouting the words. Still she paid him no attention. She sat staring stonily ahead, her impassive face registering nothing.

The preacher was a sensible man, easygoing and resourceful, but a perplexed frown clouded his face now and something akin to mild desperation gnawed at him as he contemplated his predicament.

Here he was in a strange community with an aged woman, apparently deaf and dumb, together with her load of dirty clothing and her destination unknown. It was plain she could not or would not tell him anything. Was he even headed in the right direction?

After another mile he stopped at one of the infrequent houses and hailed the clapboard dwelling where lamplight showed at a window. Hound dogs yelped. People came out, bringing a lamp. The preacher explained his predicament and asked if they knew his passenger.

A white-haired old man peered closely at the woman in the front seat. "Seems like I have seen her somewhere," he drawled. "But, I dunno, I can't recollect."

He spoke loud questions to the woman and got no response. "Maybe it's sign language she understands," he said.

With his finger, the old man pointed to the woman, to the car, and then on up the road ahead of them. The woman shook her head.

Then he described a circle with his finger and pointed back down the road in the direction from which the car came. The crone nodded in quick agreement.

"I'll have to take her back then," the preacher said. "If I can remember where I picked her up."

He thanked the people, turned around and retraced his route.

The puny headlamps helped but little in navigating the bumpy road. He had many miles to cover before reaching the place where he had found his guest. She sat there aloof, expressionless, oblivious.

After a long while the old woman shifted slightly and leaned forward to peer intently out into the gloom. Otherwise the parson never would have recognized the spot when he reached it.

He stopped the car, leaving the motor running and the headlamps burning. His passenger was already halfway out of the vehicle when he got around to her side. "You stand right here while I get your bundle," he said before he remembered that she could not hear.

His back was turned for only a second or two as he tugged the bundle of clothes out of the rear seat and turned back to face her.

But in that instant she was gone. She had disappeared.

He knew she could not have walked away. There had not been time. Besides her cumbersome gait would have prevented her from walking away without his being aware of it. He walked around the car and looked under it and inside it. Nothing. Still grasping the bundle of dirty clothes, he searched along the road in both directions and out in the bushes beside it. He saw or heard no sign of her.

Now the preacher began to doubt his senses. It felt as though drops of icy water ran along his spine. In the glow of the headlamps, he looked at his hands. Empty. His fingers were still curled, clawlike, as if firmly gripping something heavy. But the fingers were empty. The sheet of dirty clothes had vanished without his being aware of it, as had the woman.

Sounds of the night creatures came ominously from beside the road. He heard water gurgling in a creek somewhere. The moon was a cold brittle ball of ice above the treetops. Chill from more than the night air permeated the preacher now and set his teeth to chattering and his senses reeling.

"Lord, help us! Oh, Good Lord help us!" he wailed as he hastened to jump in his car and speed away from this ghostly place.

He had traveled only a few score yards when he saw lamplight at a window. Hoping to find warmth, friendliness, and shelter, he stopped.

His heart leaped with relief when the door opened under his

frantic pounding and the eyes of half a dozen members of a family peered curiously at him from behind the lamp held aloft in the hands of a husky man.

When he had warmed and calmed himself by the bright fireplace the preacher told his story. The group sat staring at him with the open curiosity of country folk who seldom have a stranger pounding on their door at night.

The woman of the house, middle-aged herself, spoke. "Would you know this old woman if you saw her again?"

"Yes, oh, yes, I'd know her anywhere," the preacher said.

The woman went to a scarred dresser, took a Bible from a drawer and extracted a picture, yellowed and frayed at the edges. She handed it to him.

The preacher's mouth opened, his eyes widened, as recognition spread over his face. "It's her!" he yelled. "It's her. This is my passenger!"

The woman's lips trembled and tears rolled down her cheeks. She sat down, shocked, her eyes unblinking.

"That's my mother," she said at last: "She only wanted to ride down here. Tonight's Monday."

"Monday?" The preacher was puzzled.

"Washday. Even at her age – and stone deaf – mother did all our family wash at her washing place on the creek bank across the road. She boiled the clothes in an iron pot, scrubbed them clean, and rinsed them in the creek. But one Monday she fell in the creek and..."

"And moved her washing to a safer place down the road," the preacher interrupted. His tone turned the statement into a plea that the dread truth he had guessed might not be so.

"Oh, no." The daughter stared for a long moment at the faded photograph, then turned frightened eyes again to the preacher.

"Mother fell in the creek twenty years ago. She drowned and we buried her in the little graveyard down the road. That's where you picked her up."

OLD JOHN'S MAGIC BALL

When Old John died in the Uwharries in the years following the Civil War, some folks claimed he was at least 2,000 years old and that the magic ball he possessed was considerably older. Just how old, no one knew. Nor will they ever. For with Old John died his secrets. All that survive today are scraps of legend and intriguing possibilities.

Both Old John and his ball are believed to have originated in the mists and dynasties of ancient Egypt – a land of pharaohs and astounding architecture, of art and culture and magic. From Egypt, Old John and his ball drifted into the groin of Africa where, many centuries later, they came by slave ship to America with stops in Georgia and South Carolina before reaching the Uwharries. Here Old John's remarkable longevity and the ball's mysterious power ran out.

Strange things frequently were seen and heard around Old John's shack in the Uwharries. Ghosts flitted in and out of the dwelling as often as did members of the small colony of black people which somehow had maintained unity through slavery days. They had grown accustomed to the oddities and attached little significance to them. Often one could hear Old John engaged in a conversation in an unknown tongue with one or more speakers inside his shack. He mumbled to himself in this same tongue while shuffling about the community in his floppy rags, the ball wrapped in burlap and cradled under his arm. Seldom did he go anywhere without the ball. Popping and cracking sounds came from the shack occasionally. Peculiar odors wafted from it. Curious lights bobbed around it and over it at night. Sightings were reported of figures of various shapes, colors and dress, hovering over and around the old man's cabin as if waiting until bidden to enter.

Despite these unusual occurrences, Old John had no lack of visitors. To his shack came a procession of the ailing and disturbed, blacks and whites, seeking help, cures and assurance. His treatment consisted of a few grunts and mumbles from an impassive face deeply etched on parchment skin, punctuated by two bright eyes and skirted with dirty gray beard. Medicine for all complainers was a common drink from a tall bowl of murky liquid. To some he gave charms and trinkets to keep on their person. Advice to the troubled was given by a nod or a shake of his head. Few ever harbored doubt or mistrust about his ability, for all who came sincerely seeking help reported improvement.

It was believed that the the magic ball had much to do with this.

The ball was about the size of an ordinary bowling ball, motley gray in color, although its hue appeared to change with the light. Pit marks, tiny cracks, seams and a faint bulge or two showed on its otherwise circular contour, dappled with a few ciphers and symbols. Shiny spots indicated where the ball had been rubbed often. Moderately heavy, it still could be carried with ease. On a mission, Old John carried it wrapped and cradled in his arm, uncovered only when in use. Never would he loan it. It wouldn't work for anyone else anyway, he claimed.

When home remedies failed on the seriously sick or troubled, these patients were brought to Old John, who scrutinized them carefully while rubbing the ball and mumbling in his unknown tongue. Most went away improved. On the hopeless, the ball had no effect and Old John informed them so with a sad shake of his head.

People battered by calamities and misfortunes and hemmed in by hopelessness and futility turned to Old John as a last resort at salvation. Most were helped materially. After a session with Old John and his ball, they returned home to find food in the kitchen, new fattening hogs in the pen, reinvigorated crops, another cow or mule to replace one that had died, bundles of clothes for the family, plus unusual good luck the next time they went hunting, fishing, trading or job hunting. Apparently all Old John did was rub the ball and mumble and assure himself and the ball that the petitioner was sincere.

Old John benefited from the ball himself. No one could remember seeing him strike a lick of work. He possessed nothing but the shack in the woods and the rags upon his angular frame. Obviously, the ball sustained him and provided nourishment, light, heat, companionship, enlightenment, entertainment and other benefits.

To many people, Old John was a savior looked upon with reverence and veneration steeped in centuries of tradition. During most of these centuries, the lips of the aged and dying whispered strange stories to eager young minds. About how Old John had been trained to operate the magic ball for the pharaohs of ancient Egypt when its power could change the destiny of nations. How though its power waned, it had kept a small group of one-time slaves and their descendants together through generations of change and crisis.

As the colony dispersed and deteriorated through faithlessness and irreverence toward Old John and his ball, so the power of the ball waned. Freedom of the slaves after the Civil War brought the final blow. Impatient for greener pastures, they departed to seek their fortunes elsewhere, leaving only a handful remaining, most indifferent to Old John. The effect on the ball was direct. It seldom responded anymore. Old John grew more feeble and haggard and it became obvious that as use of the ball declined, so did he.

Realizing the end was near, Old John tried to interest a young person in the operation of the ball in the hope that its power might be preserved for future generations. The attempt failed. Old John must have known that he started a thousand years too late on training his replacement. He knew it was improbable that he could distill and impart 2,000 years of experience into a few words and days, especially to an ignorant and unsympathetic trainee who had no inkling of the richness of the heritage, no remote idea or appreciation of the ball and its capability. So the attempt died, as did Old John soon afterward.

One of the last known requests made of the ball and its senile operator was a menial one – to help locate a missing person, a task the ball had performed successfully hundreds of times in its better days. In such cases, Old John rolled the ball along the ground or floor from the spot on which the lost one last was seen. The ball turned in the direction the lost one had taken. Additional rollings or readings could pin down the trail to a definite location or pattern.

Eb Littleton, a shiftless laborer, had been missing for some days. However, his wife and several small children did not appear unduly concerned by his prolonged absence. People knew him as a lazy drunkard, heartless and cruel to his family, for whom he provided only haphazardly. As the mystery of his absence became more puzzling, Eb's relatives searched futilely through the forests and in nearby communities for a trace of him.

Then, heartsick and despairing, they sent for Old John and his ball. Eb's wife told Old John, as she had told other interrogators, that the last time she had seen her man was when he left the room one morning to go out to see about work. That fixed the starting place for the ball.

Old John, dressed in his customary ragged trousers and floppy jackets, uncovered his ball and stood against the far wall of the big room. He faced the open front door. A small fire sputtered in the ash-clogged fireplace across the room to his left. An unmade bed looked soiled and smelly. Garments were draped on dilapidated chairs. Old John made ready to roll his ball. Outside the door, a small group of interested onlookers waited to see which way the ball turned.

On the first roll, the ball seemed to hesitate before it reached the door. It veered off to the left and struck the wall beside the door. Its momentum spent, it stopped there.

Several people watching through the doorway crowded closer. Were the old man's hands so feeble and his eyesight so poor that he could no longer aim the ball properly? A hint of surprise showed on Old John's face.

Slowly, he retrieved his ball and resumed his original position. This time, as if he already knew what would happen, he rolled the ball deliberately slower.

Before it reached the middle of the floor, it began to execute a slow almost 90-degree turn, heading straight for the open fireplace in which a few red coals gleamed and a sporadic blaze flickered. The ball rolled onto the hearth and came to a stop touching the heap of ashes overflowing the fireplace.

Gasps of surprise and shock came from the onlookers, some of whom crowded into the room. Old John looked stunned. Eb's wife looked at the position of the ball. Her eyes grew wide. Her hand flew to cover her gaping mouth. She staggered backward to a wall and leaned against it.

"Thet ball of yourn has gone haywire, Old John," complained skeptics in the group. "Eb cain't be in the fireplace and he cain't go up the chimbley. It must be lying. Try rolling it again."

They made way for Old John as he raked out his ball, warmed now from the firecoals, and went back to his position. Adjusted to the conditions now, he rolled the ball again. As before, it started out straight for the open door, but again veered off toward fireplace, stopping in the ashes. At the demand of those who scoffed, Old John rolled his ball twice more. Each time it started out for the door, but appeared to be pulled by some mysterious force which sent it spinning in a sweeping arc for the fireplace.

"It's the devil!" screeched Eb's wife as she ran toward the fireplace. "It's the devil come tuh git me in that thing!"

With a final scream, she reached the fireplace, snatched up the ball and, snarling furiously, hurled it violently away from her. The ball ricocheted off the ceiling, struck the top of the wall, then fell to the floor with a jarring thud which shook the room.

Unsteadily, Old John sagged to his knees on the floor to grope for the pieces of the broken ball. Under each eye, a tear left a wet track across the leather of his face.

Eb's wife confessed in a wailing voice for all to hear.

Yes, she had killed her no-good husband. Killed him with an ax while he lay sleeping drunkenly in his bed. Then, late at night, she used the axe to hack the body into little pieces which she burned to cinders in a hot blaze in her fireplace. Yes, his ashes were still there in the fireplace.

Legend has it that inflamed relatives of the dead man grabbed Eb's widow and rushed her off to the woods where they held a private lynching party.

Some time later, as a visitor approached Old John's shack one evening, ghostly figures fled like quail from the wayside. He found Old John sitting in his chair by a cold fireplace, no warmth or life in his body. Stiffened hands still fondled pieces of the broken ball in his lap. They say his emaciated body and mummified face were hideous to behold.

The pieces of the broken ball were buried with the body of Old John. Some sentimental person shaped a stone in the approximate size of the magic ball and placed it against the marker on his grave to keep him company. But no one knows where this grave is anymore. It would take something more powerful than a magic ball to locate Old John's remains today, Uwharrie people say.

One of the most frequent ghostly noises reported by Uwharrie folk is the loud clatter and banging made by something like a full dishpan dropped on the kitchen floor late at night. Yet, when investigation is made, nothing is disturbed and no reason for the noise can be found.

"Must've been Old John's magic ball a-crashing to the floor," some elderly householder may murmur.

They claim it's possible still to see, in and around the Uwharries, the nocturnal ghost of Old John, out on a mission, winding up and letting fly his magic ball which is apt to land most anywhere. A few Uwharrians even believe that on the nights when prowling ghosts are most plentiful a keen observer can spot one or two whose garb and demeanor are conspicuously foreign to any of the native ghosts. They are thought to be the restless ghosts of pharaohs coming to search endlessly in the Uwharries for a missing magic ball stolen thousands of years ago from their tombs in Egypt.

OL' HEAVY
AND THE RIVER TRAIL

Philas, the fiddler, left his home at dark one Saturday night in the early fall to walk two miles upriver and cross over to play his fiddle for a square dance. Known far and wide as a man who sawed thumping good square dance music from his instrument, Philas was a bachelor in his forties, a sturdy man of good health and even temperament. He had no cause to be alarmed as he tucked his fiddle case under his arm and started on the mile-long wilderness path along which nobody lived.

Guided mostly by instinct and his familiarity with the path, Philas had gotten into the thickest part of the swamp when he heard a rustling in the bushes beside the path.

Thinking it the wind, he walked on. But the sound came again – unmistakably the noise of someone or something pushing heavily through the brush and trees adjacent to the path.

He stopped. "Who's there?" he called.

Nothing but the still night and gentle breezes answered.

He walked on and the noise resumed. He slowed and the noise slowed. When he walked faster, the noise grew faster. Slow or fast, it kept pace only a few arm lengths away to his left.

Again he stopped, a tightness clutching his chest.

"Who is it? What do you want? Why don't you speak?"

Silence.

A few faint stars peeped through the tree branches. Frogs croaked soulfully. A disturbed owl scolded the intruders. The nocturnal gloom of the creepy swamp settled down oppressively.

Philas started running this time, hoping to dash ahead of the noise, but it ran along with him.

At this point, he knew, a lake of still water lay on either side of the narrow path. Yet he heard no sound of splashing.

Philas speeded up, thinking he might lose his pursuer at a sharp turn ahead. But after he rounded the turn and got into full running form again, the crashing in the bushes took its place to his left again.

With half a mile yet to go before he reached the Mosely cabin near the river crossing, he decided the best thing was full flight ahead. So he broke into a headlong run, jumping logs, dodging over-hanging limbs, occasionally stumbling and falling in the blackness.

But the sound bulldozed its way through the thickets with ease, keeping up with him.

Exhausted and wild with excitement and fear, Philas slammed into the door of the Mosely cabin, fell inside, and gasped for some-body to fasten the door.

Minutes passed before he could talk. Mosely, his wife and chil-dren stared at him as if he were some wild animal invading their home.

When his breath came back, he shakily told what had happened on the trail. "You better spend the night here with us," Mosely said, "Tomorrow we'll go back and take a look in the daytime and see if we can find some sign of what it was."

But a fiddler with a waiting audience is a hard man to dissuade. "The folks are waiting on me," Philas said. "I've got to go on."

Mosely handed a lighted kerosene lantern to Philas.

"Take this. Maybe it will keep boogers away till you get there."

Philas picked up his fiddle case, took the lantern, and walked out the door.

He reached the edge of the porch and started down the steps when a wave of overpowering nausea hit him. He reeled, staggered backward, and fell inside the door unconscious. Mosely dragged him away from the door and bolted it. They couldn't revive the fid-dler so they put him to bed and he did not come out of his daze until morning.

Philas breakfasted with the Moselys, then got his fiddle and went back through the trail in the swamp in the bright and clear Sabbath morning. Mosely accompanied him part of the way.

They examined both sides of the trail. On the side from which Philas had heard the noise, they found smashed and twisted bushes, sheared saplings, torn vines and branches – a path large enough to accommodate an elephant.

Mosely trembled violently. His voice turned hoarse and shrill. Philas grew shaky and unnerved when he realized how close he had been to this "thing" capable of such destruction. They sent word to other men in the community to come with their dogs and guns and search the swamp.

Expert woodsmen and hunters examined the trees and broken twigs carefully for signs of hair, fur, or flesh, some clue to the identity of the thing. But they found no sign at all. Neither were there tracks in the soft and wet ground. Yet the men left deep prints of their own. Their hounds growled and whined but failed to pick up a scent.

Later, other men in the neighborhood reported hearing the same noise as they walked along the swamp trail at night. They heard no footfalls or splashing, yet the thrashing in the bushes kept abreast of them.

Someone called the force "Ol' Heavy." And the name stuck.

Some thought Ol' Heavy to be a savage beast. Others figured it had to be an otherworldly creature. Whatever its nature, it would appear now and then, then retreat to the swamp and lie dormant for long periods.

After the path was abandoned and Ol' Heavy had been unheard for decades, hunters prowling the river wilds one autumn day happened upon a startling sight. They saw a long, round, almost symmetrical tunnel stretching through the thickets. Inside the tunnel, growth was stunted, dwarfed by the verdant forest around it, and looked as if it had been had been that way for many years. The hunters could only marvel at the phenomenon, until in telling a long-time resident of the the area about it, he recalled tales of a frightful but unseen swamp creature that folks once had called Ol' Heavy.

THE PREACHER-BUGGY TREE

Preacher Calvin Stamey had a certain tree where he hitched his horse and buggy in the churchyard of Lane's Chapel Church in that part of the Uwharries between the Uwharrie and Yadkin rivers. Each Sunday morning when he arrived at church he tethered his horse to an iron spike driven in the side of the big oak tree. No one ever questioned his right to the hitching place and it always awaited his coming.

Folks say it was interesting to watch the old man's arrival.

He sat ramrod straight in his buggy seat with his head erect and his chin thrust forward. Snow white hair showed under his black felt hat. His spectacles kept jostling down on his thin nose. He looked like a statesman in his dark frock coat with his stiff white collar and black string tie. Usually his arms were shoved straight out in front of him where his big fists grasped the leather reins that guided his horse. A big Bible lay on the seat beside him.

Seldom did his head move, and he looked straight ahead. He wasn't one to see or wave at people along the way. And it was not because he was snooty or superior, but because his mind constantly dwelt on heavenly things.

"Ole Uncle Calvin Stamey was called by God," the hill people said. "He was always occupied with the Lord's work."

The splotched gray roan had learned to jog trot to suit the old man's temperament. And the animal had grown so accustomed to the preacher's habits and trips he practically knew where they were going before they ever left home. The clippity-clop hoofbeats of the horse on the hardpacked country roads identified the traveler before he came into view. No other buggy horse had developed quite the same rhythm of footwork.

So on Sunday mornings a good fifteen minutes before time for church to take in, you could look for the horse and buggy and driver to come around the bend into sight of the church. Buggy leather creaked as the wheels crunched over fragments of flint dotting the churchyard.

Though it was unnecessary for the well-trained roan, Preacher Stamey "whoaed" him and pulled back gently on the reins as the buggy left the road and angled off toward the tree. The horse stopped with his nose nudging the oak. The preacher alighted stiffly, tied the lead rope to the spike, then claimed his Bible from the buggy seat. Only then was he ready to acknowledge and greet the groups of waiting church people.

For years on end this ritual was repeated each time Preacher Stamey came to church. People began to time him and set their watches by his arrival. Most people got to church early in those days to fellowship around the outside before entering for the long services. They would listen attentively to hear the first hoofbeats of the roan's fancy jog trot and then watch with loving eyes the familiar details of the preacher's arrival.

One youngster in his early teens who watched the arrival of the old preacher for several years was Charlie Cagle. Charlie was a member of a church-going family and he often helped Preacher Stamey hitch his horse and brought water to the roan from the church spring.

The old man appreciated the boy looking after his horse. "You're a good boy," Preacher Stamey would say to Charlie. "I'll remember you, son. Yes, sir, I won't forget you."

He wondered then what Preacher Stamey meant about not forgetting him.

Charlie was only nineteen when the old preacher died late one winter after a long siege of pneumonia. He helped dig the grave in the church cemetery and he stood in the afternoon sunshine the next day and watched a team and wagon haul the preacher's casket to the church for the funeral and burying.

The years passed and other preachers came and preached at the little country church. None ever equalled the dignity and grace of old Preacher Stamey, nor his disdain for the devil, nor his fiery condemnation of sin and deceit, nor his praise of God and righteousness. As the years passed, cars began to replace the buggies and wagons in the churchyard. Grass grew over the hitching places. An iron spike in the side of a big oak lost its sheen and grew rusty.

Twenty years rolled by and Charlie Cagle still lived in the community and passed by the church frequently. A married man now with a family and a good reputation, Charlie farmed and sawmilled and he had kept the church-going tradition of his forebears.

One night Charlie visited with a neighbor until late bedtime and walked back down the road toward home. He passed by the church and decided to stop for a drink of water at the church spring. Bright moonlight bathed the countryside in a soft glow almost bright as day. Everything seemed to slumber peacefully.

Charlie finished his drink and leaned against an old hitching post to enjoy the refreshing air and the tranquility of the moment. He listened to an owl hoot mournfully from somewhere in the woods back of the church.

Then another sound registered faintly in his ears. Clippity-clop. Clippity-clop-clop. He wondered what horseback rider or what horse-drawn vehicle would be traveling the road at this hour. He stepped nearer the road so he could identify the traveler.

Clippity-clop. Clippity-clop-clop.

Suddenly, the flesh tightened at the base of his neck. The blood chilled in his veins. Those hoofbeats had a strangely familiar ring.

They were nearer now and clearer.

There was no mistaking them, Charlie's insides churned in turmoil. They were the hoofbeats of the roan horse that pulled old Preacher Stamey's buggy. His heart beat wildly now as he stood rooted to his tracks with his head turned up the road from whence came the sound.

The prancing hoofbeats drew nearer and a dark shape drifted slowly down the road toward the man, who was now immobilized by fright. His startled eyes identified a horse and buggy.

Then the buggy came out of the shadows and into the bright moonlight.

There on the seat sat old Preacher Calvin Stamey, his head thrown back and his outstretched hands holding the reins that ran to the splotched gray roan.

Charlie's numbed mind told him it was Preacher Stamey, absolutely him, just as if time had abruptly jumped back to a Sunday morning twenty years ago. He saw the old man sitting there ramrod straight. There was the dark hat, the white hair, the frock coat, the high collar with the string tie and the spectacles slipping down his aquiline nose. There lay the big Bible on the seat beside him.

All these things Charlie saw as the buggy approached him and passed within three arm lengths. The old preacher looked neither to the right nor left, but straight ahead. Harness leather creaked. Charlie swore later he even smelled the sweaty odor from the jog-trotting horse's body. The spinning buggy wheels crunched over fragments of flint as the roan angled off the main road and headed toward his customary hitching place at the big oak tree.

Charlie turned as the buggy passed him and watched fascinated as it began to slow nearing the tree. He heard a "whoa" come from the buggy and saw the roan's head raise in response to a gentle pull on the reins.

But then another incredible thing happened before Charlie's wild eyes.

Instead of stopping, as he always had done before when he reached the tree, the roan continued. He and the buggy and its occupant turned straight up the trunk of the tree and vanished among the twisted branches.

Charlie rubbed his eyes and shook his head to clear his befuddled mind.

He lurched out of his tracks and staggered a few paces forward. He whirled and looked up and down the road. He peered into the branches of the big oak, well outlined in the moonlight. There was no buggy or horse or man up there. Nothing at all. The moon smiled down at him and the night was again still. All he could hear and feel now was his ragged breathing and the pounding of his heart.

He ran all the way home and burst in upon his family and babbled to them about this strange sight he had witnessed. He began jerking in a severe chill, and they put him to bed where he continued to shake in spite of the blankets they piled upon him.

Next day, recovered from his shock, Charlie repeated his tale over the community. People did not dispute his word for they knew him as a man addicted to the truth. They were convinced that he had indeed seen what he described so realistically.

No one else ever reported the phenomenon of this dead preacher riding in his buggy only to vanish up the moonlit branches of the hitching tree in the churchyard.

But Charlie Cagle saw it and he continued to tell people about it for as long as he lived.

Always, he interpreted the experience as fulfillment of the old preacher's promise of remembering him – even from beyond the grave.

THE GHOST
ON TOP OF THE GRAVE

Julie Ann was nine when her dress caught fire from flames licking around the washpot outside her home. She ran into the field screaming and blazing. Before her hysterical mother got to her and snuffed out the flames with her bare hands, the little girl was unconscious, badly burned all over her body. Later, pneumonia set in. The child lingered for three weeks before she died.

Her mother blamed herself for the tragedy. So great was her concern for the child and so painstaking were her ministrations during the critical illness that she practically had gone without sleep and food the entire time. From the moment Julie Ann breathed her last until the neighbors arrived to comfort her, the frail mother beat at the cabin walls with frenzied fists. Her screams and moans rent the air. Finally, she sank to the floor in grief and exhaustion.

Neighbor women laid out the body and someone left to take word down river to Preacher Stymie Stoker to come and conduct funeral rites. The preacher had visited in the sick child's home once with words of encouragement, and he had preached in the community church and married several of the couples there, including Julie Ann's parents.

He remarked later that this was the most grueling funeral he ever went through. A sizeable group of bareheaded and longfaced mountain people stood around the grave while he tried to tell them about God's love for the little ones, and how He had plucked this flowering little girl to brighten His Kingdom, and how she was much better off there in the splendor of Heaven. He talked as soothingly as he knew how of love, of God's mysterious ways, and about how we should not question His judgment at a time like this but should so adjust our own lives that we, the survivors, could be a living tribute to the memory of this precious little one who had gone on.

The father of the dead child shed tears unashamedly as did many other mourners. But the mother, beyond tears now, moaned steadily between two stout women who supported her limp frame. Her pallid face and sunken eyes mirrored the burden she bore.

Clods were smoothed over the mound of earth and bouquets of wild flowers were placed on it by the younger people. A man with an axe drove a temporary wooden cross into place. When his additional words of comfort failed to help matters with the sorrowing parents, Preacher Stoker departed, telling other people he was on his way to High Falls, far on the other side of the Uwharries, to hold a week's revival for a preacher friend.

It must have been nearly midnight when he came back through the community more than a week later after a long and tiring drive. But he felt good and chipper and his old mare was holding her wind, so he decided to drive on home through the crisp night rather than awaken some household and seek lodging. He recognized the mountainside graveyard where he had conducted funeral rites for the dead child a few days earlier.

The preacher's eyes were drawn to that fresh grave. What he saw caused him to doubt his senses. Hairs rose on the back of his head and a chill shook him to the marrow of his bones.

Something long and bulky and white covered the dark grave.

No other grave contained any such object. Was it flowers? No. A sheep or a big dog? It was neither.

The preacher felt his heart beating wildly. He tried to quell the frantic messages of fear shooting to his brain. As a realistic man, he knew there must be some logical explanation for this wraith of white over the new grave.

He pulled his skittish mare to a halt off the road and tied her to a sapling. With his nerves steeled and his mind made up, he turned back to the grave to see what was there.

It was in the same place, and it didn't stir as he walked closer.

He slowed, watching cautiously for a movement or a sound which might offer some clue to its identity.

Closer he inched. And closer still. Now he could see it plainly in the moonlight. But all that he could make out was something white, bulky and still.

Finally he stood over the new grave. He was close enough to bend and touch this thing, which he planned to do if it did not reveal itself first. He braced himself, gritting his teeth, and reached out his right hand, fingers opened wide. Whether the object proved supernatural or human, he was determined to find out.

His hand went down, down, slowly, apprehensively. He bent forward. Then his hand touched something...something soft and yielding, but firm.

His fingers now grasped cloth and he pulled. Revealed now was a dark patch. He bent closer and his fingers explored again.

Now it looked and felt like a woman's luxuriant head of hair. It was a woman's hair! That's what his hand had touched – hair. His taunt nerves relaxed a little.

He felt for her shoulder and shook it gently to determine if the body connected to this head of hair was alive. He felt movement awakening under his hand.

Then slowly there stood erect in front of his astonished eyes a woman dressed in a flowing white nightgown reaching to her ankles. Her white nightcap, pulled away by his tugging fingers, sat crookedly on her head. Apparently, she had been hunched down on top of the grave on her knees and legs with her head bent forward into the fresh earth of the grave. The nightgown and nightcap had covered her doubled-up form completely.

As she stood where he could get a good look at her face, Preacher Stoker felt cold alarm plunging through him and his tension mounted again. Instant recognition leaped into his eyes.

The woman in white standing trance-like on top of the grave was the mother of the dead child who lay buried beneath her feet!

Obviously she was still asleep. Walking in her sleep, he thought. Probably her turmoil had been so great over the loss of her child, coupled with her emotional and physical breakdown, that she had gotten up from her bed in her sleep, walked to the grave and collapsed on top of it to be near her dead daughter.

For a few seconds he debated whether to awaken her, knowing she would go into hysterics when she became aware of her surroundings and what she had done. He must help get her back home the best way he could.

He took her by the shoulder and waist and walked her to his buggy. He untied the mare's tether, picked up the woman and put her on his buggy seat, wrapping the heavy woolen lap robe around her for warmth and to help subdue her. He guided the mare back up the road. She sat stolidly. He wondered if the poor woman wasn't mentally unbalanced by her lengthy ordeal and how she might be affected if she awakened to find she had been on top of her daughter's grave in the middle of the night .

The buggy pulled up at her home and the preacher rapped and halloed, bringing her husband and others scurrying to the door in their night clothes. In one hand the man held a lighted lamp, in the other an old Army musket.

"Amos, it's me, Preacher Stoker. I was passing the cemetery on my way home and saw something peculiar on top of little Julie Ann's grave. I went up there and looked and it was your wife, Mabel, curled up on top of the grave in her nightgown. Must've been walking in her sleep. She's numb and dazed. I got her in the buggy and brought her back, thinking you maybe hadn't even missed her yet. What she needs is rest and quiet after the ordeal she's been through. A long, long rest. You leave her alone, Amos, and let her rest and take her own time about adjusting. Come on, let's get her inside and back to bed."

Amos' eyes were big and sad and frightened.

"Preacher, you been gone fer a week and couldn't know..."

His voice faltered and tears fell from his eyes.

"...my wife died on Monday. We couldn't wait till you got back, so we went ahead and buried her there in the cemetery close to little Julie Ann. That was three days ago."

The preacher reeled around, mouth agape, heart and mind palpitating anew, and stared at the buggy. The lap robe lay crumpled into a heap on the empty seat.

GUARDIAN GHOST WIND

When the wind shrieks around the eaves of my hilltop home I visualize a lonely and beautiful spot in the Uwharries where the wind howls and performs in a way perhaps unequaled anywhere else on earth. Standing there on the brink of Jumping Off Rock, I listen to the swishing creek down below and it tells me to look west where another big rock juts out of the hillside. This is the lair of the ghost wind of the Uwharries....

"The Yankees are coming – hide everything!"

This message was heard in the Uwharries, as elsewhere through the South. Bruised farm people were cautious and fearful as the Civil War's noose of destruction and deprivation tightened around them. What little sustenance remained could not be allowed to fall into the despicable hands of the invaders from the North.

Silas Meekaps was crippled. His two strapping teenage sons were a little too young for Army service, so the father gave the boys a special chore: to take his lifetime hoard of gold coins into the deep woods and hide it where the Yankees would never find it. Guard it well, he told them, and when danger had passed, they could reclaim it.

Putting the gold in an iron pot and wrapping the pot in a sack, the boys slung it on the handle of a mattock and lugged their heavy burden into the woods. Eventually they spotted the boulder amid the trees on the mountainside and decided to bury the gold at this landmark.

Merritt, the older boy, was on his knees scraping the last dirt back in the hole over the treasure, then covering it with leaves and pine needles to disguise it. Sandy, the younger son, stood behind watching and wrestling with an idea that blazed through his immature mind. If he, Sandy, were the only one who knew the location of this gold, then he could come back someday and claim it all for himself.

Impulsively, Sandy seized the handle of the mattock and swung the tool mightily around over his head. The heavy metal end struck his kneeling brother in the back of the head, killing him instantly.

Merritt sprawled, jerking and kicking, blood from his crushed head crimsoning the dead leaves. It looked as if the dying boy tried to rise and speak to his brother, but convulsions shook him and he flopped to one side motionless. Sandy rolled the body of his brother down the steep mountainside into a thicket. He flung the mattock after it.

Then a peculiar thing happened to Sandy. He went berserk.

The sudden realization of the enormity of his act – murdering his own brother – snapped his mind and he ran off into the forest yelling and screaming. For the remainder of his life, Sandy flailed trees with his arms and hands, gnawed bark and ate leaves and berries, a raging and ferocious imbecile totally unable to communicate.

More than the horror of war gripped the Meekap household in the days that followed. The devastation was plain to see in Silas's haggard face, in the heartbreak dripping from the glazed eyes of his wife, Maude, who forever after wore a badge of grief symbolized in an uncontrollable jerk of her head. Their future security had evaporated with the presumed death of one son, the loss of the family gold, and the other son a vicious maniac who roamed and bellowed through the Uwharries, his presence more dreaded by the householders than a grizzly bear. Until their deaths, the Meekaps blamed it all on the Yankees.

Neighbors tried to sympathize materially with the crushed family. Groups of men occasionally subdued Sandy and pinned him in a stable or room until he beat his way out again. Time and again they organized search parties to comb unsuccessfully through the woods and hills for signs of Merritt and the Meekap gold. Wily ones watched and followed crazy Sandy, hoping he would give them a clue or lead them to the right spot, which he never did. Years later, an uninformed hunter shot and killed Sandy, mistaking him for a wild animal.

Eventually, another a hunter discovered bleached human bones, a tarnished belt buckle, scraps of decayed leather on the side of the mountain. Nearby was a rusted mattock, its handle rotting away. Everyone agreed this must be the spot. Merritt Meekaps must have died here. The gold must be hidden nearby.

So the search began again and the search continues intermittently.

Most searchers concentrate their efforts around the big boulder farther up the mountainside, figuring the youths buried the gold at the base of this rock. Many have come and searched here, but no one has recovered the treasure. Because a remarkable thing happens when you come here and start digging into the ground at the bottom of this big rock.

No matter how still and windless the day is, if you start digging near this big rock, the wind starts rustling the leaves and sighing in the pines. If you keep digging, the wind gets stronger. If you dig more, the wind gets stronger still until it screams at you around the rock. And if you persist in digging, the wind becomes so strong it literally blows you away from the rock and tumbles you down the mountainside.

Uwharrie people identify this fierce wind as the ghost of Merritt Meekaps, still carrying out the mission assigned by his father to guard the gold until all danger was past.

People say if you listen closely enough when the wind starts, you can hear the maniacal cries of Sandy Meekaps just the way he screamed that awful day after the murder when his mind snapped and he went tearing off into the woods to live like an animal.

When I heard this story while doing research in the Uwharries, I could not rest until I had visited this location. My guide led the way through brambles and brush choking the rough terrain near the foot of the small mountain. Then we climbed to this rock and I photographed it, made mental notes and looked for signs of digging around the bottom. I visualized what happened here on a day perhaps much like this day near the end of the Civil War. Too, I could understand why visitation and interest had waned in this isolated site.

Only then did it occur to me that we had not brought along anything to dig with and activate the guardian ghost wind. I kicked around in the leaves at the bottom of the rock for a while but nothing happened.

Dozens of times I've planned to go back, even had a pick and shovel in the trunk of my car, but something always arises to prevent it. Others have reported similar situations. It seems the guardian ghost knows when a repeat visitor is coming back to dig and the ghost nips such visits in the bud.

But newcomers evidently can get to the site without interference. Therefore, if you plan to dig, come prepared on your initial visit, because the way things apparently are you might not be favored with another.

GHOST IN THE PORCH ROOM

Aunt Mattie Grissom, an affable, middle-aged widow, worked as a practical nurse, midwife, and companion to invalids all across the Uwharries. Folks loved her, welcomed her, and rated her right up along with the doctor and the preacher in social standing. Anything Aunt Mattie told was considered gospel.

Her unexplained abrupt departure from a country home in the Newsom area where she was employed to care for a bedfast invalid puzzled people for a long time. Finally, after a second employed woman left the same household under similar circumstances, the two got together and told why.

Sleeping quarters for the employed woman at this household consisted of a small room on the end of the porch, common on country homes half a century ago. The cramped room contained only a bed, dresser and a chair. Upon leaving the room early each morning, the woman locked it, kept her key and usually did not return to it again until bedtime, when she locked the door behind her.

Each night upon lying down to sleep in that room, Aunt Mattie could feel a pair of hands begin rubbing over the outline of her body outside the bed covers. Each night when this happened, she got out of bed, lit the kerosene lamp and searched the room, finding nothing to explain the strange activity. The door and window were securely fastened. There was nothing under the bed and no other place for anything to hide.

After the first night, Aunt Mattie kept a stick and would strike

out with it, flailing the air, whenever she felt the hands rubbing her body. But the stick never collided with anything and it didn't ward off the fondling hands.

A few nights of such ghostly monkeyshines was all Aunt Mattie could stand. She left without telling her employers about the odd occurrences.

Later, she met her successor in the porch room, a staunch elderly mountain woman, who likewise became alarmed and departed the premises after a few nights of experience with the bothersome hands.

Each related a similar account and each corroborated the other's version of the activities of the ghost with the wandering hands, a mystery which has gone unexplained to this day.

THE GHOST OF JEZEBEL

Not long after nightfall one fall evening in the early years of this century, 12-year-old Isaac Efird burst into the door of his parents' home in the mill village on the western edge of Albemarle and sobbed out an incredible tale.

A large, shaggy looking white thing – a monster – had molested him on the path through the swamp on his way home from his job in the nearby cotton mill. The thing followed him aggressively, and tried to get him to follow it, before it attempted to shove him off the path. Then, as he neared the edge of the dark swamp, the boy saw the white shape galloping straight at him as though determined to knock him into the water. Numbed by fear and cold, the boy fell prone as the shape passed over him and vanished. He scrambled up and ran home hysterically.

"Papa, it was trying to hit me and kill me, weren't it?" the boy asked, still shaking from fright. "I first saw it at the creek and it tried to push me in. Then it tried to knock me off the path and then it tried to run over me. It's mean and it's mad at me and it's trying to hurt me, Papa. I don't wanna go through them dark woods by myself. Don't make me. That thing'll get me."

Leland Efird tried to soothe his son. He looked at his wife, Clara, whose eyes flashed fire as she transferred the boy's head to her breast. "Do something, Lee," she said stonily. "Do something."

Leland put on his coat, got his gun and lantern, went outside, called his dog and headed for the swamp.

The swamp, which lay between the mill and the cluster of houses, was about a mile long by a quarter-mile wide, bordered by a creek on the side nearest the mill. Several footpaths meandered through it. Leland walked all of these and tramped through the thickets on the dry end, but he saw no strange white shape. Nothing unusual at all.

But other people did. In succeeding days many people walking the paths to and from the mill before daylight and after dark reported seeing the ghostly white shape acting as if it wanted to attack them, particularly the children. Any children walking through were sure to be approached by it. It got so bad parents wouldn't let their children go there alone. Men carried guns with them on the paths. Reports were that some fired into the shape without effect. When workers formed groups to pass through the swamp, the white thing leaped at them from concealment and bounded away before anyone could take action.

Was it a particular person, or child, the white thing sought?

After his first encounter, Isaac approached the swamp in great fear, even when accompanied by his father or friends. He tried to avoid the paths in darkness, waiting until dawn to walk to the mill and leaving to return home before dusk. Even then, the white shape still darted out after him and others, sending them fleeing in fear.

Great alarm stirred the people. Couldn't the mill company do something? Couldn't the law do something?

Wasn't there some way to rid the swamp of the fearsome white thing? But repeated daytime searches of the swamp failed to turn up anything.

A man who had seen the white thing close up remarked in Leland's presence at the mill one day that it looked just like a big ghostly sheep. Leland thought about that all day on the job. Then he remembered. And knew. Leastwise he was pretty sure he knew. His hands shook on the machinery the remainder of his shift. That evening on his way through the swamp he silently cursed the white apparition he knew was lurking in the thickets, watching, waiting for the right opportunity. That night after Isaac had gone to bed, Leland sat at the supper table blowing pipe smoke at the glowing lamp chimney. And he told Clara the story, as he could recall it, that had come to his mind in the mill that day.

His great grandfather, Tobian Efird, once owned the land where the mill and the village stood, as well as hundreds more surrounding acres. Tobe, as he was called, had four sons. The youngest was Ishmael, his favorite.

"The older boys resented their father's attention to the young boy and they schemed up ways to put Ishmael in a bad light," Leland said. "And Ishmael was scared to tell his father the truth for fear his older brothers would work him over. They took Ishmael with them and forced him to take part in their mischief. Stuff like rocking the ducks on the pond, disturbing the chickens roosting in the trees, driving the rooting hogs into the cornfields, and puncturing melons on the vine. On Sunday afternoons some of the neighbor boys joined them and they'd git back down in these creek bottoms out of sight of the house and chase the sheep and pester and torture them just for pure old mean devilment. One sheep they always beat the worst was a big ewe named Jezebel.

"One time they run Jezebel so hard they hemmed her up in a corner of the rail fence and she got trapped there.

"The big boys beat her unmerciful with sticks. They stoned her some. Then they sicked the dogs on her and the hounds chewed her up some. They got tired of the fun and left, leaving the tattered sheep there in the fence to suffer. But Ishmael stayed because he felt so sorry for the sheep. He looked around till he found what had the sheep fastened and freed her. But Jezebel mistook his intentions and thought he was one of her tormentors. Pawing and kicking, she charged him time and again and Ishmael had to duck behind the fence till she gave up and left. You don't often see a vicious sheep – they're a gentle animal – but they say old Jezebel turned awfully mean after that and would charge Ishmael every time she seen him.

"Tobe knew it, of course, and tried his best to keep them separated. But one day it happened. Ishmael was twelve that fall and he liked to fish for catfish down here in this creek. One afternoon he and Tobe were fishing for cats in the deep hole when visitors arrived up at the house and Tobe had to leave the creek. He let Ishmael stay on after he didn't see the sheep anywhere. After a little while at the house, Tobe came back to see about Ishmael and just as he rounded the barn and came in sight of the creek, he saw this shape come crashing out of the bushes straight at the boy. It knocked him off the stump and into the dark water. Tobe yelled and hollered as he run, but he was too late. Ishmael was drowned and dead by the time Tobe got there and got him out. And Jezebel had vanished.

"Ol' Tobe nearly went crazy with grief and a craving for revenge. He got his boys and his guns and his dogs and his lanterns and pine torches and searched for Jezebel day and night. They kept searching on and on, just stopping long enough to attend funeral services for little Ishmael, then right back. But they didn't find the ewe, even after a bunch of neighbors volunteered to help them look. But they knew she was still around, because now and then she would lunge out of the thickets and try to attack one of the other boys when they'd be walking alone in the swamp. It must have been weeks later, maybe months, before old Tobe, still searching every day, finally stalked up on Jezebel in the woods and shot her dead and left her carcass laying there for the buzzards."

Leland Efird looked across the table at his wife's taut face and pleading eyes.

"Lee, you don't think...this thing that's after little Isaac, you don't think it could be...no...please...."

Her wide eyes mirrored fear. A white hand trembled at her mouth. Leland slumped moodily in his chair.

"I've heard my father say that his father told him that he had repented long ago of his part in all that meanness and mischief and torturing that got blamed partly on little Ishmael. But that don't help us none here. What's that old saying about the sins of the father sometimes being passed on to the son?"

Agitation increased over the ghost sheep in the swamp and its attacks on walkers. Exaggerated tales were circulated and many superstitious folk believed them. There were reports that the ghost sheep devoured all children it reached; that even one touch from it marked you for death. Men said they got close enough to kick it and strike it with sticks without "feeling a thing." Growing evidence of personal encounters indicated the phantom sheep was form without substance.

But what did it want? What was it after?

It clearly wanted Isaac Efird, to do him bodily harm. This soon became obvious to everyone. Every time the boy went in the swamp, no matter how many people accompanied him, the ghost sheep tried to get him, being foiled only by the men and other people clustered around the lad. Some of these escorts reported contact with the ghost but said they felt nothing. This being the case, could the sheep harm the boy even if it got to him?

Isaac and his parents knew that it could – and would. As the ghost grew bolder in its attacks toward Isaac, the boy's fear mounted. He almost had to be subdued and carried through the swamp. He knew that, to him at least, the sheep meant death. He could feel it and told his parents so. Leland and Clara realized they couldn't bear much more of this strength-sapping fear and suspense. They had to take some action right away. But how did you fight a ghost sheep unaffected by stones or sticks or bullets?

Fishing for cats in the deep hole in the creek continued to be a favorite pastime for the villagers. Leland and Isaac often fished there. One Saturday afternoon when the mill stopped early, a group of men and boys, Leland and Isaac in their midst, went fishing at the creek, the boys running and yipping and the men laughing and talking loudly. They spotted the ghost sheep lurking in the bushes. After an hour around the fishing hole, some of the group began to leave. Finally only two remained, a large fisherman and a small one. As the sun vanished behind the trees, Leland wound his line around his pole and walked away, leaving the small fisherman perched on a stump intently regarding his line in the water. The figure wore the familiar leather cap and the overall jacket with the red collar in which Isaac almost always dressed on chilly days such as this.

Soon the sheep materialized from the woods and galloped straight for the little fisherman on the stump. Its forepaws shot out and thudded into the back of the figure, which toppled forward, splashed into the water and sank out of sight. For a moment, the ghost sheep stood watching, then turned and trotted away, vanishing into the thicket.

It was next morning before Leland and his friends came back to recover the weighted figure from the deep hole – a dummy carefully made by Clara to resemble her son Isaac, who had inconspicuously returned home the previous afternoon with the first of the departing fishermen.

The ghost sheep appeared no more.

Paved streets have replaced the footpaths of the swamp. Electrical substations, a parking lot and a ballpark have been built upon it. Industry, business and dwellings press in upon the remaining patch of woods. Few people walk the swamp anymore – except the many boys who come to play ball. If anyone looks for ghosts in the swamp today, it's usually from the safety of the motor vehicles which cruise the area.

However, some people in the community still believe that the ghost of old Jezebel, the evil ewe sheep, continues to prowl the swamp area looking for another young victim and that you're likely to see it most any night when a youngster's around. And if the night has just the right touch of atmosphere attractive to the spirit world, folks claim you can see the ghostly figure of old man Tobian Efird, gun in arm, stalking Jezebel in vengeance of his little lost son.

But the big question the oldtimers have is this:

Isaac Efird lived to raise a family and see many fine grandsons. Almost three generations have passed since Isaac's experience with the ghost sheep. One of these years will that old saying about the sins of the father hold sway and will a young descendant clamor home some dark night with a horror tale about a ghostly white shape molesting him while walking near the creek?

Some think so, even though they may not be around to see it.

THE CRYING BABY

In the half dozen years they had lived in their new farm home on the southeastern edge of the Uwharries, Eric Austin and his young wife, Mabel, often had heard the heart-tugging cries of a pleading, tormented infant coming to them out of the night from a tumbledown shack at the edge of the woods nearly half a mile away.

At first, after their initial investigation revealed nothing, they had not paid much attention to the plaintive wailing drifting to their comfortable home. They were too preoccupied with getting settled and with planning and dreaming about the sturdy sons and daughters they would rear. But after the children they longed for so passionately failed to come, they attached more significance to the eerie cries of the ghostly baby.

Sometimes the sound drove Mabel, a sensitive and intelligent woman, to bitter tears which her husband could do little to curb, though he approached his wife with tenderness and understanding.

"It's mockery," she sobbed. "The crying mocks us because we're childless. I wish I could hold that crying baby in my arms and comfort it. I could make it stop crying. I know I could, because I would love it so much."

And then she would say wistfully, "If I only had a real baby of my own to love." And more sobbing came.

Many times, Eric, occasionally accompanied by his wife, visited the tattered cabin to try to figure out the puzzle of the baby cries, which had attracted and mystified many people.

The plain old house had been lived in by a forgotten succession of occupants who both loved and loathed it. Hardly anyone could remember the name of the pioneer family that had built the house. Other dwellers had rebuilt and changed the cabin to suit their tastes. It became a way station at which people lived until they could do better.

One hazy fragment of memory survives about a pretty young woman, pretty but sad, who lived in the old cabin many tumultuous years ago. Alone? The twilight of years has erased the answer. Although many families with abundant offspring buffeted the old house since the time of its building, the memory of the sad young woman edges to the forefront of reminiscence about it.

The sound of the crying baby caused many curious visitors to marvel and wonder. Likewise, it shortened the stay of the latter-day occupants. Gradually, the notoriety of the ghostly sound scared away prospective inhabitants. Then decay set in.

Eric agreed with other visitors that there was no mistaking the sound. It was exactly like the erratic whine and wail of a disturbed and neglected baby, sometimes fading, then rising to a peak of fretful screaming. Skeptics said it was only the wind hissing like an assassin through the trees around the cabin. But the sound could be heard on the stillest of days.

Checking into the history of the place, Eric found the property ownerless and heirless, so he acquired it by paying the back taxes. Afterward, during slack times in his farming, he felt free to come to the cabin and examine it carefully while his wife sat outside in the sunshine watching him moodily.

He discovered the sound of the crying baby followed a pattern. When he entered the musty confines of the cabin, the sound appeared to come up through the floor from the dugout cellar he knew to be under the house. So he would go outside, push aside the briars and vines, enter the dark, cobwebby cellar and listen. Then the sound seemed to be coming from above.

Eric wondered if the answer did not lie somewhere in the floor. This could only mean one place – under the fireplace or hearthstone. For the underside of the floor was bare and some of it had rotted away. He looked at the hearthstone, a smooth-topped slab of native slate around which many a family had warmed itself and over which many a meal had been cooked. Rotting timbers had caused cracks to widen around its edges and one corner sagged beneath the level of the uneven floor.

Some strange attachment seemed to draw Eric to the cabin time after time. He began to wonder if the ghostly forces which dwelt in the old house had not somehow chosen him as the key to unlock the secret of the crying baby.

One blustery winter day, Eric got two young men to help him examine the fireplace. Armed with pry bars, picks, and sledge hammers, they began to tear at the stone. They had made only a few exploratory jabs when the scarred hearthstone yielded with surprising ease. It proved to be only a thin slice of stone which one man could lift. It would have been an easy task for a woman to have lifted one end of the stone, they reflected later.

Eric stooped to study the shallow, dusty cavity revealed under the hearthstone. Poking in the rubble, he found something which brought gasps of astonishment from the other two men.

In his hands he held small decaying bones and the fragile white skull of a tiny baby.

Immediately, a feeling of serenity settled over Eric. His body relaxed and his face softened as his eyes looked heavenward to grope for an understanding. He knew the crying baby never would be heard here again. Already the atmosphere of the shack seemed less hostile. As the men departed the place, the winter wind in the trees around the lonely cabin expressed itself in fierce relief.

"That good feeling of peace came over me all at once as I held those little bones in my hands," Eric told his wife later that day. "It was a good feeling. One that makes me know we won't have any more worries coming from that place."

A sound of another crying baby entered the Austin household a year or so later – the lusty cries of a healthy baby boy.

THE SHEEP-STEALING GHOST

This mild moonlit night would be ideal for sheep stealing, Murphy Pate told his rangy sons, Jasper and Duncan. The younger sheep would be easy prey as they frolicked away from their tired mothers snoozing in the pasture. Pin their fore and hind legs in either hand, drape them across your shoulders and over your neck, then get away fast. Try to get the fattest ones first, of course, for they made the best eating.

So an hour after dark, the boys approached the Hezikiah Barnhardt farm, off on a lonely Uwharrie road, where sheep, the major livestock grown, baa-aaed in droves. They paused amid the tombstones of an old family graveyard beside the wagon road. Across the road and a little further on lay the sheep pasture. Beyond it, out of sight around a bend in the road, was the Barnhardt residence.

Duncan decided to keep watch from this vantage point among the tombstones while Jasper went ahead to get the sheep. As his brother left on his mission, Duncan hunkered amid the dozen or so whitish tombstones to watch and wait.

Stars glistened brightly and soon the moon would edge into the heavens. A hound dog yowled at a farm house over the way. Far off across the valley came the faint sound of the choir practicing at old Calvary Church. Every few minutes, Duncan would rise and peer around to see if all was well.

Ambling down the road by the graveyard came Claude Trevor,

whittling on a whoopee stick, on his weekly visit to see Uncle Hezikiah. Something made Claude, a robust, cloutish fellow, look over at the graveyard.

Hey! What was that?

He saw a whitish shape rise up and weave about the tombstones. A ghost? It had a man's shape all right. It moved again. Claude knew it must be one of the corpses arising from the grave and a-coming to get him. He'd heard tales of such happening. He waited to see no more, dropped knife and stick, and lit out running.

A few minutes later, he flumped onto the Barnhardt porch, beat against the door and yelled to be let in.

"A ghost, a ghost! I saw a ghost. Up here in the graveyard. A real one. Plain as day. I saw him rise out of one of the graves and go weaving about like he's looking for somebody. Had a man's shape. I swear it. Let's go back and look, Uncle Hez. I want you to see it, too. Quick, before it leaves."

"How am I gonna git up thar'?" Uncle Hez asked. "You know my rheumatism ain't let me walk none for ten years. It's too much trouble to hook up the mule to the wagon. 'Course I don't believe a word of it nohow."

"Then I'll carry you on my back. I want you to see it so I can prove I saw it. Hurry. Let's go while he's still up there."

With the old man on his back, Claude hurried back up the road toward the graveyard.

Crouched among the pale monoliths, Duncan grew impatient. Wasn't that slowpoke brother ever returning with a sheep? Then he relaxed and stood erect as he watched a bulky and awkward shape loom into the graveyard from the road. He took a step or two forward.

"Is he a fat one?" he asked cautiously.

Both Claude and his uncle had seen this spectre rise from the grave and stride toward them. Now they heard it speak. Claude began trembling all over. His rider gripped him fiercely around the neck and shoulders, his skinny legs scissoring into his midriff.

When he could muster his voice, Claude said, "No, he's not fat, but you can keep him anyway if you'll leave me be."

He pawed the frantic, screaming old man off his back and shoved him toward the figure at the grave. Then he wheeled and ran as hard as he could go down the road to the Barnhardt dwelling – only to find that Uncle Hezikiah had beaten him back and, though breathing hard, was urging him to get inside and bolt the door fast before that ghost got them.

FOOT RACE WITH A GHOST

One of the favorite ghost stories of the Uwharries concerns a hungry tramp who stopped one winter evening at an abandoned house on an isolated road to build a fire, warm himself and look for something to eat.

As he thawed before the fire, munching a crust of bread from his pocket, the tramp saw a man with no head appear through the far wall and walk over to join him at the hearth.

"It's been quite some time since I've had the pleasure of receiving a guest like you in my home," remarked the man with no head, offering his hand.

The tramp's eyes flared wider and wider as he looked the apparition up and down. "You won't have me long," he screamed and lunged out the door, slamming it after him.

He ran headlong down the trail for three miles before he collapsed on a log to catch his breath. He had just begun to relax when he glanced to one side and there stood the man with no head, his foot nonchalantly propped on the log.

"Quite a race you're putting up this evening, old boy," said the headless figure.

The tramp grabbed his old hat off the log, his feet churning.

"Friend," he said, "you ain't seen nothin' yet."

THE GHOST
WITH THE FLASHING KNIFE

Lucinda Jane, the six-year-old girl swinging on the fence gate, had no inkling of the few minutes of horror she would witness that October morning in 1865 in eastern Stanly County. It scarred her consciousness and caused nightmares the remainder of her long life. Every time she returned to this homeplace location, now abandoned and obliterated for decades, she claimed she clearly saw a ghostly reenactment of this fatal drama.

"I could see that long knife a-flashing up and down, again and again," she said, shivering. "I always had to leave, because I felt like it was coming to get me next."

Nobody doubted what Lucinda Jane said she saw, initially or later.

To accuse a man of stealing your hog was the next thing to calling him a hoss thief – the ultimate in epithets – among the struggling, war-tired people of the South in the uncertain days at the end of the Civil War. Such an accusation meant a fight, bloodshed, and harbored hatred that often erupted in murder.

It did lead to murder in Stanly County – a murder with one of those ironic twists that fate injects into the picture to make the whole thing look so futile and unnecessary.

Conditions were chaotic. Crippled Confederate soldiers were back home helping with the farming for the first time in five years. Returned veterans and their families tried to patch together enough sustenance for survival and to re-adjust themselves to a land so ravaged by war that often no tools were left with which to work. Against this background of privation, a family hog, even a nondescript old razorback hog, was a valued possession, one that caused considerable alarm when it turned up missing.

Bushrod W. Lilly, 63, had several hogs on his farm. He prized them highly as meat for his family. When winter's meat-preserving cold arrived, he planned to butcher his hogs and salt them away in the smokehouse. He was an upstanding man, respected and looked to for moral leadership in the community during the war.

His neighbor, Al Carter, had a reputation for trouble making and plundering. Carter was dark and swarthy. Folks said he had Indian blood in him. He was the type who harbored ill will in his heart and magnified trivialities until they became obsessions. He bullied people when they protested his outlawry.

When one of Lilly's hogs didn't show up for a day or two, Lilly let it be known that he thought Carter had stolen the hog, probably butchering it by night and selling or trading the meat to people who asked no questions about its origin.

Carter heard the accusation and his anger flared. He wasn't the type of man to ignore finger pointing. There had to be a showdown.

On the morning of October 18, 1865, he shouldered his longbarreled muzzleloader, fastened his wicked, homemade hunting knife to his belt, and walked eastward across the fields to Lilly's home.

Bushrod Lilly sat in his log corn crib shelling corn. He looked out through the logs and saw Carter coming. There was no time to run home for his gun.

Carter stopped before the open crib door and looked inside at Lilly. The muzzle of his long rifle, cradled in his arm, pointed directly at the seated man.

"I hear you been telling people that I stole your hog," Carter said, his bleak face showing no emotion, his eyes blazing.

Lilly looked into the muzzle of the gun. His chin quivered. But his voice was firm. "Yeah," he said. "I been saying it. You did steal my hog."

Carter's mouth twisted into a snarl. "I've come to kill you if you don't take that back and tell folks that I didn't steal your hog."

"You did steal my hog," Lilly maintained. "I ain't taking it back."

Carter brought his gun up in firing position, aimed it squarely at

Lilly's heart and pulled the trigger. But he purposely pulled the barrel up and the bullet struck a log above Lilly's head.

"You can't scare me like that," Lilly said. "You ain't gonna kill nobody." Then Lilly laughed loud and mockingly right in the gunman's face.

The laugh drove Carter into a frenzy. Dropping his useless rifle, he screamed curses at Lilly and drew his hunting knife. When Lilly saw the flash of the knife, he bolted out the door and ran around the crib with Carter in hot pursuit, slashing at him.

At the paling fence between the crib and his log house, Lilly tripped and fell, sprawling on his stomach. Carter pounced upon him and drove the knife into his back again and again. He pulled the wounded man into a sitting position and stabbed him some more.

Unknown to either of the two, Lucinda Jane was swinging on the fence gate within a stone's throw of the two men. She saw everything. The scene made an indelible impression on her young mind. "The big knife, it went clean through Mister Lilly and come out on the other side," she told people later.

Carter, his fury abated by his dripping knife, stepped over the body of his victim and glanced wildly about him to see if anyone had witnessed the fight. Had his eye fallen on the little girl frozen immobile to the gate, the fearsome knife might have shed more blood. Carter ran off along the fence until the woods swallowed him.

Hysterical, Lucinda Jane ran to the house where she was met by the women, who, alarmed by the shot, were coming outside to investigate.

They got Lilly inside on the bed before he died. His blood dripped on the floor boards and for years afterward, the occupants said the bloodstains would never wash away.

Bushrod Lilly was buried in the cemetery of what is now Badin Baptist Church, the inscription on the marker reading: "B.W. Lilly, born June 9, 1802; died October 18, 1865, age 63 years, four months and nine days."

A day after they buried Lilly, the mourning folks around the Lilly household had a new touch of grief added to their burden. They heard grunts and squeals coming from the edge of the forest and saw a fine, razorback hog trotting happily into the yard. It was the lost hog Lilly had accused Carter of stealing.

Years passed and nobody saw anything more of Carter. Rumors were that he had fled out west to Indian territory.

At night, folks claimed, you could see a light hopping along the rail fence where Al Carter had run following his dastardly act. Some years after the murder, people searched along the fence and found the murder weapon. The handles had rotted and the long blade was tarnished with rust.

Five years passed, maybe ten. Al Carter was largely forgotten except for oldsters who liked to tell the story of the murder around a blazing fireplace at night while the wind moaned outside in accompaniment to the scary tale. An occasional curious person came and looked at the blood on the floor and the bullet hole in the log at the crib.

Then a message came that electrified the community. A man thought to be Al Carter had been spotted by a local man visiting out West. Inquiries were made by local officials. Enough evidence accumulated to convince officers to make the long trip. They found the suspect's farm and saw him plowing.

"Watch him, boys," an officer said. "If he stops and spits when he gets to the end of the row, that'll be him."

Sure enough, when the man got to the end of the row and started pulling his team of mules around, he turned and spat tobacco juice at the bushes.

"That's him," the officer affirmed. "Let's get him."

Carter offered no resistance. They returned him to jail in Albemarle. A former friend of Carter's visited him in jail and said the man was unbelievably aged. His hair was snow white, his face wrinkled and gaunt, and his body thin and emaciated.

"If remorse, heartbreak, pleading, sorrow and repentance would bring Bushrod Lilly back, he would have been back and alive a long time ago," Carter is reported to have said in his cell.

He told friends who visited him that he had hardly seen a moment's peace since he killed Lilly and left the county. Thoughts of his terrible act had plagued him always and tormented his dreams. Whatever they did with him now, he said, couldn't be any worse than the punishment he had already endured from his own conscience.

A beaten and contrite old man, Carter was found guilty and the judge sentenced him to life in prison, where he died within a few years.

As an adult, Lucinda Jane revisited the location of the killing and said she could see the ghostly knife reenact the murder so realistically that she covered her eyes and wheeled away in horror as she re-lived those awful moments.

Other people reported seeing unusual flashes of silvery light, like glints from polished metal, in the vicinity of the murder site.

What happened to the knife, the actual murder weapon, no one remembers. But stories handed down over the years indicate that the knife, or an apparition of it, is still active. One man stopped at night on the road closest to the location and reported he saw the knife floating in the air. It became so menacing – an arm started slashing with it – that he drove away as fast as he could without ever looking back.

More recent sightings make one thing plain.

If you fool around this site too long the flashing knife in the upraised hand of the troubled ghost of Carter himself will chase you away. He wants no witnesses to the grisly crime that is destined to be reenacted here throughout eternity.

HEARSE WAGON GHOST

Aunt Cora Calvert had been sick and mostly bedfast for two years before Doc Medlin told her husband, Uncle Cromer, the sad news: her illness was incurable. She probably never would get any better, though it was certain she would get much worse. And it might be years before the end came. All anyone could do was be patient and good to her and try to make her last days comfortable.

Uncle Cromer tried. But his heart wasn't in it. An active, wiry outdoorsman and farmer, he found it disagreeable to spend so much time inside ministering to the sick woman. Some of the children helped. A married daughter came home occasionally and cared for her mother. But mainly, it fell his lot to wait on her and calm her fear of impending death.

She awoke at night and screamed nightmarishly about the old hearse wagon coming to get her. She ranted and raved. She knew she was slowly dying. She thought every sound was Demon Death coming to snatch her away.

Though he stayed and ministered faithfully, Uncle Cromer longed for the sunny fields, the creekbanks and forest slopes where he stalked deer, bobcat, wild turkey and coon.

Another year passed. Aunt Cora grew thinner and weaker. She became petulant and demanding, realizing she could get her way and taking advantage of this special treatment. She demanded tidbits to eat and niceties of care which Uncle Cromer had neither the means nor inclination to satisfy. This made her mad and pouty, full of accusations that he deliberately mistreated her and wished her dead. So nasty grew the sick woman's vituperation and lashing tongue, that neighbors knew they could never satisfy the taunting whims of her disease-warped mind. Their visits became less frequent to this little cabin beside the flinty wagon road which led on up to the community church in sight on the hillside.

Yielding to sudden impulse, Uncle Cromer killed his wife late one afternoon while misty haze hung over the valley and mourning doves lamented the curtailment of the day. He justified this mercy killing to himself by the fact that she could never get well, that it would put an end to her intense suffering, that she was better off, that it would remove a burden from himself, his family and the community.

He did it with a big, fluffy, feather pillow pressed tightly over her face.

She knew. Her eyes burned defiantly at him. Her mouth curled in a sneer. Her tongue berated him. She struggled until the pillow smothered the last breath of air from her.

When Uncle Cromer first began applying the pillow, a noise outside temporarily distracted him. A wagon approached. Distinctly he could hear the crunch of iron-rimmed wheels over the gravel, the creak of harness leather, the plopping of horses' hooves on the firm earth, the rattling of the wagon bed. He listened as the wagon creaked to a stop near his front door.

"Maybe it's that blamed old hearse wagon you've been dreaming about, coming on to git you now," Uncle Cromer said, forcing the pillow into the woman's face with savage force.

Despite his strength, she freed her face enough to spit these venomous words at her husband: "If it's the hearse wagon, it will surely come back one day and get you, too."

Soon her struggling ceased and he removed the pillow from the dead woman's face. He smoothed the pillow, replaced it and straightened her rumpled hair and gown. The, he went to the door to see who had come.

But no one was there. No sign of any horse or wagon or person. As he looked, the wagon noise resumed as before, beginning within a few steps of his door, and continuing on out of hearing up the road toward the church. But he saw not a thing.

The mysterious wagon noise coupled with the imprint of his wife's last words began to trouble Uncle Cromer.

No one suspected anything unnatural about his wife's death. Women came and laid her out and men built a pine box coffin and dug a grave in the churchyard. Next afternoon, a real hearse wagon crunched into the yard, waited until the corpse was loaded, then rattled away to the open grave exactly as the unseen one had done.

Uncle Cromer resumed some of his carefree roaming in the fields and woods. He farmed only enough to provide the necessities. Life was better now, but much less perfect than he imagined it would be. The sound of the ghostly hearse wagon continued to plague him. Many late afternoons, especially when wisps of fog and haze swept through the valley, he and anyone who happened to be present could hear, but never see, the wagon and horse crunch into the yard, pause near the door, then resume and fade away toward the church.

Everyone who heard it said it sounded just like the hearse wagon which came to get Aunt Cora and haul her away to the graveyard.

Loneliness forced Uncle Cromer to take another wife. Always he had admired Cora's younger sister, Viny, and now he married her and brought her to the cabin to live. The younger wife produced children who brightened the old man's life. As the children grew older, he disciplined them with threats that the old hearse wagon would come to get them if they disobeyed. The sound of the unseen wagon wheeling in and out of the yard emphasized the threat and the children didn't know but what their father had the power to make the ghostly wagon really appear and whisk them away.

Age and exposure fast began to cripple and wither Uncle Cromer. Arthritis and gout twisted him and racked his joints with pain. Then tuberculosis began to deteriorate his insides. Pneumonia left him flattened and emaciated. Viny had to wait on him hand and foot, enduring his vile tongue and abuse. The old man took fiendish pleasure in censuring his wife for failure to adequately provide for his needs and grant his whims. His disposition degenerated into such violent hostility and acrimony that visitors stopped coming inside to see him, but rather sat outside until Viny had time to come out and report to them on his condition.

Each time the ghostly wagon noise rolled up toward the door, Uncle Cromer heard it and trembled. Sometimes he screamed wildly, "She's sending that hearse wagon to git me like she said she would. That's why we still hear it. It's waiting to come and git me."

Then he convinced himself that Viny was going to kill him because of his meanness to her and to put him out of his misery. Every action she took in his room, he regarded with suspicion. He refused to let her come close to his bed, made her eat some of his food before he would eat. He asked for some of his best friends to come to his beside where he whispered to them his dark suspicions about his young wife. None of them believed him. Some told Viny what he said. Let him rant, she told them, for long ago she had learned to ignore his coarse mouthings. Doc Medlin warned them that the old man might go any day.

Each time the unseen wagon rolled into the yard now, Uncle Cromer claimed he could hear the gloating voice of his dead wife, though no one else could hear it.

"She says she's coming to git me in the hearse wagon for what I did to her. She laughs about it. She's gonna git me the same way I got her, she says. She says there's no way of escaping that hearse wagon."

As was their custom late in the afternoon toward the latter part of the week, a few neighbors sat outside the cabin door waiting for Viny to come out with a report on Uncle Cromer's condition. Plumes of mist formed weird shapes in the low places under cloudy skies.

Inside, Viny attempted to minister to an obstreperous old man who was sure she meant to kill him to avenge her sister and so she could take a virile young husband. She seemed more solicitous. Her eyes appeared to gleam wickedly. He cringed when she looked at him, shuddered when she started toward the bed.

A horse-drawn wagon began to clop and crunch into the yard.

"It's her! Here she comes to git me in that hearse wagon. And this she-devil sister of hers is gonna have me ready to go when she gits here."

He opened his eyes to see a smiling Viny approaching while fluffing up a big, feather pillow in her outstretched hands.

The men outside were startled to see the wildly screaming old man half crawling, half dragging himself through the door and onto the little porch where he stammered something about someone coming to get him. Then, he collapsed and lay still in death.

As the men gathered around him, the wagon noise resumed and they turned to listen as it rattled out of the yard and faded up the rocky road toward the church – a performance genuinely reenacted the next afternoon with Uncle Cromer on board.

All Viny could tell them to explain the old man's last frenzied action was that he had gone into uncontrollable fear when she approached the bed with a fresh feather pillow to put under his head.

GHOSTS OF THE TIMECLOCKS

"There..listen..that's him! Can't you see 'im? I can. I can feel 'im. I can see 'im. He's coming through right now! He's clocking out for the last time."

Never clocking in. Always clocking out – for the last time.

An eerie message in an excitable voice from a tense and emotionally charged individual.

Always in the wee hours of the morning.

And always followed the next day by the news of the death of the person the narrator claimed he could sense and see.

Incredible? Yes.

Yet, it happened not once or twice but half a dozen times or more.

No precise documentation exists, and no in-depth research has been attempted, but memory authenticates the strange story of Ol' Shug and his prophetic visions of impending death.

"He did it. I know he did it. I saw him and heard him do it. Several times."

So affirms Roy (Goody) McKinney, who as a first-aid attendant, worked closely with Shug at Alcoa's Badin Works plant in the little town of Badin on the western fringe of the Uwharries.

Shug worked as a third-shift janitor in the big "washhouse" building, lined with lockers, where the production workmen washed up and clocked out on the timeclocks as they came off their shifts in the aluminum plant. One part of the building was used as a combination guard house and first-aid station with close proximity to the timeclocks and locker area.

"Anybody coming through the locker area or using the time-clocks, we could see them and hear them easily," McKinney recalled. "Especially in the quiet, wee hours of the morning. Sometimes it was...just...unearthly quiet."

That's when the timeclocks became activated by invisible persons or entities.

Invisible but not unknown.

"Shug knew who was doing it," McKinney says. "It only happened when Shug was around. Or, if it happened at other times, it didn't register on us."

There's no mistaking the metallic "clunk" of a timecard being punched, according to McKinney. Not after you've heard it thousands of times.

"Shug usually got finished with his cleaning-up work early and he'd come in the first-aid station and sit down with us," McKinney said. "He did this many nights. It would be about 2:30 or 3 o'clock in the morning. Quiet, quiet. Nothing going on. Shug couldn't stand to stay by himself in other parts of the big ol' dark building. He wanted to be near somebody else during those lonely wee hours. He was afraid of storms, too. Thunder and lightning got him all shook up. He said he was afraid of dead people, too. We laughed and picked at him about his fears."

The distant rumble of a thunderstorm brought Shug into the haven of the first-aid station on one such night.

"The storm never did get close, but it was enough to make Shug uneasy and crave some company," McKinney said. "He sat there in his chair almost dozing. Then I saw his head jerk up. His eyes grew big and full of alarm. His mouth opened in surprise. His whole body was tense. He looked like he was ready to bolt. I know these symptoms of shock and fear and trauma, because we deal with it a lot in first-aid."

Ol' Shug rose warily to his feet while staring at the timeclocks.

Both of them heard the distinct "clunk" of a timecard being punched.

They looked at each other.

"Lord a-mighty, it's him!" Shug cried. "He's here right now.

Right here clocking out. I can see 'im. I can feel 'im. I can see his feet down under the partition. Can't you? Can't you see 'im, too? Come on, he's so plain you gotta see 'im. Ol' man Smith. You've seen 'im come through here thousands of times. I have, too. Well, this is his last time. He's clocking out for his last time on this earth."

McKinney remembers how Shug looked after each such ghostly encounter.

"His face was a picture of mortal fear and terror and bewilderment. Concern and sorrow, too. I have no doubt that he was actually seeing and living what he described. He seemed to be genuinely sorry that he had to witness such a sad scene and report such bad news. But he was convinced what he saw there at the timeclocks was real. Also, that he had to share it with the rest of us. He'd always tell us just wait till next day and we'd find out he was right."

And Shug was always right, too.

"Next day, we'd hear the news about a death the night before. Ol' man Smith had actually died. Or whoever it was that Shug had seen coming through the timeclock. Always it was some longtime employee who had worked in the plant most of his life and used these timeclocks every working day. Most of them were elderly people who had worked for the company thirty to forty years. Some had already retired. Some were out on sick leave. Some may have been in the hospital. All these deaths were natural and not unexpected. None was associated with violence, as I recall."

Ol' Shug has been dead for many years now. He died without revealing any more details about his mysterious ability to see and hear the ghosts of dying people punching out one last time on their earthly timeclocks.

"After the first time or two he did this, we questioned him about how he did it, but he never would tell us," McKinney said. "Probably he didn't know how he did it and couldn't tell us. He was puzzled that we couldn't see and hear and sense all that he could."

McKinney reflected a moment.

"Our timeclocks occasionally made an extra little jumpy noise. Anyone who works around timeclocks much knows this. We referred to that extra little noise as the timeclocks 'catching up time.' Some people tried to tell us that this 'catching up' noise was all that Shug was hearing. But that can't be so. No, it was real."

Was Shug ever worried over his strange ability, or about whose ghost would be coming through the timeclocks next, foretelling a death in the community? Maybe one of his friends?

"His ability to see the ghosts of these dying people didn't seem to upset him any, except while it was happening," McKinney said. "At work was about the only time I ever saw him. If he had any other unusual gifts I don't know about them. I never knew him to wonder or speculate about who might be next."

He shook his head.

"I'll never hear a timeclock without thinking of Ol' Shug and his ghostly timeclock punchers."

Wonder if Ol' Shug's ghost came through the timeclocks or wandered through the big washhouse building on the night he died?

"I've thought about that, too," McKinney said. "I don't know. I still wonder about it. If Ol' Shug's ghost did come through the building when he died, it must have been disappointed, for nobody was there who could see and hear it the way Shug used to."

WITCH
TALES

THE SQUEAKY PINES

Even today people who know the story are cautious about driving alone at night down Rocky Hill Road in the Rocky River area of the Uwharries. Though nothing untoward has happened there in a long time, nobody knows when history might repeat itself.

Leland Gaddy was one of the first to tell about the goblins at the squeaky pines along the road.

Years ago in a howling storm, two tall pines were partially uprooted and fell into each other's arms, their massive bodies wedged together. They continued to grow in this unusual fashion. When the wind blew, even a mild wind, the trees became musical, rubbing together in a tortuous squeak-squawk monologue.

One gusty, moonshiny night, Gaddy drove down the hill in his buggy and had gotten close enough to hear the pines squeaking when he saw something he had never seen before.

The body of a man swung gently by his neck from a rope tied to a tree limb sticking out over the road. He could see it plainly. The man's feet were bound and his hands lashed behind his back. About the time Gaddy jerked his roan horse to a stop, the apparition vanished.

Then a horrible little creature appeared on the dashboard of his buggy, regarding him with piercing, almost human eyes.

"Are you going to stop at the squeaky pines?" the creature asked.

Gaddy yelped in alarm and struck at the goblin with his buggy whip, which went right through the creature's body without effect. Frantically, Gaddy struck again and again with the same results.

The squat, dark creature had tusk-like teeth, a hairy face, long arms and claw-like hands. Its speech was guttural, but understandable.

"Are you going to stop at the squeaky pines?"

Suddenly, more goblins appeared. Two sat beside Gaddy on the seat. Two more joined the first one on the dashboard. Gaddy could only stare in wonder.

"The witches will try to get you to drive on past, but you'll die and join that man in the tree if you do so," the first goblin said. "We want you to stop, turn around and go back the way you came."

But Gaddy was so befuddled that just before he got to the pines, he wheeled his horse and buggy off on a little side road leading to the Gramp Dunlap place. As soon as he left Rocky Hill Road, the goblins jumped off his buggy and vanished.

Wilson Secrest had a similar experience on the road. As he approached the squeaky pines, he saw the dead man hanging from the tree limb just as Gaddy had described. Then it vanished. Three witches with hook noses and pointed chins, all wearing black shrouds, appeared by the roadside.

"Drive on, drive on." they cackled, waving the buggy onward. "Nothing's here to hurt you. Drive on. Drive on and be away with you!"

But Secrest declined, wheeling his horse and buggy off at a fast gallop down the Gramp Dunlap Road.

For years afterward, travelers going down Rocky Hill Road at night claimed they could see the hanged man swinging from the tree limb. Then they were approached by either the goblins or the witches – never both at the same time. The former warned them of the witches' deceptive invitation and advised them to turn around and go back to save their lives. The witches insisted that the travelers pass by and disregard what they had seen. Nobody ever dared continue on. Neither could anybody figure out a reason for these apparitions until Uncle Mitt Howard, patriarch of the community, remembered a story which helped explain the curious situation.

Years ago in slavery times, an old man whose name Uncle Mitt couldn't remember owned an empire of land in the area and scores of slaves. He was cruel and heartless to his slaves, beating and abusing them. He once whipped a slave to death with a chain as a lesson to others. The man's three spinster sisters lived with him, and they were as cruel as he was.

After enduring their owner's sadistic torture for years, the slaves rebelled one day in a remote corner of the plantation. A group of them jumped their master, subdued him, and stretched his neck from a limb of a big tree on the rocky hillside. He swung there for two days before he was found. No one ever knew how it happened.

For the remainder of their lives, the three sisters sought revenge for their brother's death, but they finally died with their mission unfulfilled.

Uncle Mitt figured that the goblins were the ghosts of the slaves and the witches were the ghosts of the hanged man's sisters – the goblins coming back to win sympathy and justification for lynching their cruel master, the witches to get revenge for their brother's death.

As more and more travelers saw the ghostly lynched man and found themselves accosted by the goblins and witches, fear grew. What if the witches actually got somebody?

That possibility grew stronger after Gramp Dunlap got fiery mad about so much extra buggy traffic waking him up at night and decided to put a stop to all that tomfoolery up at the main road. He strung a barbwire fence right along the main road, put up a gate across his road and padlocked it every evening.

"Now, dadburn it all, let's see which way they go," Gramp said. "No dern use of so much traveling by here at night, anyway."

News about the new fence blocking the escape route spread fast and it discouraged local travelers from using that part of the road at night. But what if some stranger should happen by unawares? Or somebody had no choice but to travel Rocky Hill Road at night?

One night Cleo Burroughs beat on the door of Doc Anderson's house near bedtime. His wife was trying to deliver and complications had set in, Cleo explained. He needed the doctor – and quick.

While Doc got his gear together, Cleo hitched Doc's horse to his buggy and tied his own to the back so that he could ride with Doc.

"Which way did you come?" Doc asked him.

"Up the Rocky Hill Road. And I didn't see the ghosts because I came up the hill. But we'll have to go back that way and down the hill, Doc. There ain't time to go no other way."

Doc drove. Once before he had seen the apparition on Rocky Hill Road. To be on the safe side, he had detoured off like everyone else. Now with Gramp Dunlap's road closed he'd have to try something new if a crisis developed. And he had little doubt that it would. The white-faced boy beside him was brave, yet he gripped the edge of the seat rigidly and stared ahead as if expecting to meet Judgment Day head on.

When they started down the hill toward the squeaky pines, Doc urged his horse into a fast trot, hoping to whiz past before the ghosts could bother them.

Just then Cleo recoiled in his seat. "There it is, Doc! Gawd-a-mighty, there it is! They's two of 'em!"

As the ghost of the hanged man appeared over the road, a second body swayed ominously beside it.

"It means death if we go on, Doc," Cleo said. "That second body up there means it'll happen sure." Sobs of futility shook his frame, as the buggy began slowing, then stopped.

The five goblins hopped aboard, crowding the buggy, and the three witches materialized beside the road.

"Turn around and go back," urged the goblins. "The witches will send you to your death if you listen to them. Already there are two bodies swinging from the tree. Do you want to make it four? Turn and go back."

"Drive on, drive on," the witches clamored in unison. "Pay no heed to these hideous creatures. Don't be frightened by what you see. Drive on. You won't feel a thing. Drive on, drive on!"

Fierce determination blazing on his face, Doc Anderson gritted his teeth and half rose to give his horse a terrific wallop. The animal lunged forward at a gallop, yanking the buggy along.

Simultaneously, the goblins fell out with cries of distress and vanished before they hit the ground.

The witches disappeared in a big puff of smoke.

Though it had been a serene night until now, a great tumult erupted as the buggy came alongside the squeaky pines. A shaft of flame struck at the buggy. A deafening explosion jarred the ground.

The squeaky pines began a slow, grinding, limb-ripping crash, then lay smoldering on the ground.

But the buggy sped on past, its occupants safe. When Doc pulled the buggy up to the Burroughs house, he found he had another patient – Cleo, who shook with uncontrollable chills and shock. A dipper of brandy from a stone jug helped settle him. And even Doc took a quick snort to relieve his tension before he set to work to save the life of the mother and her unborn child.

No more were the ghosts, goblins and witches seen on Rocky Hill Road.

But for years afterward, long after the squeaky pines had rotted away, old folks said you could see three crows perched in nearby trees, silently watching all passersby. Now and then they would swoop down and try to catch five little field mice that regularly scampered around that spot in the road.

THE WITCH
IN THE PIG LOT

Farmer Silas Stokes leaned on his hog lot fence smoking his homemade pipe filled with homemade tobacco and watched his herd of a dozen swine tear into their morning ration of ear corn and slop from the house. Yep, there was that strange one again. Almost every morning for two weeks now he had noticed this strange brindle hog in his pens at feeding time. It was of a different breed and coloration and had a different temperament. He watched this strange hog, more greedy and aggressive than the others, shove its way to the front to eat a large portion of the feed.

This hog wasn't satisfied until it had violently competed for every last grain of corn or scrap of food. Then for as long as Stokes watched, it stood around aloof and independent, refusing further association with the swine herd.

The strangest part was that the hog disappeared later in the day and couldn't be seen again until the following morning at feeding time. This fact baffled Stokes and he spent much time trying to figure out the riddle.

How did it get in and out of the hog lot when none of the other animals could? For that matter, why didn't it return to the lot for the late afternoon feeding since it appeared to be so hungry?

He had examined the enclosure thoroughly. There was no possibility the hog could come through the rail fence without leaving some sign. Its chances of climbing or jumping the fence were remote. His practice was to close the gate each night against predators and to open it and turn loose the hogs for foraging after the morning feeding.

Lately he had been keeping the swine penned longer each morning to observe the newcomer.

This morning he watched for an hour after the hogs had finished eating. The brindle hog ambled about placidly, a little apart from the others. Stokes felt as if the hog regarded him calculatingly from its beady eyes. The hog had a tawny hide diffused with dark spots. All the animals now were grunting and oinking in growing impatience to get out of the cramped quarters into the open fields.

The warming sun made Stokes decide to walk down to his spring at the foot of the hill for a cool drink. He would release the hogs on his return.

He was gone only for about five minutes and out of sight of the hog pen only for about half that time. Nevertheless, when he returned to the pens, the brindle hog was gone. It had disappeared.

Alarmed, Stokes looked in every corner of the pen. He checked the fence. He walked all the way around it and looked in every direction. There was no sign. The hog had vanished.

As he headed back to his log cabin to tell his wife, he glimpsed someone walking along the wagon road in sight of his home. He knew by the faded ankle-length skirts, the wrap-around sun bonnet, her posture and manner of walking that the figure was old lady Rennie Coble, an irascible old soul who lived alone in a rundown house a ways down the valley. Frequently she was seen trudging along the roads and trails and asking people for handouts, gathering wild herbs for her "witches brew" which she concocted on request as treatment for ailments. It wasn't uncommon to see her anywhere in the community at any time doing anything.

Disturbed over the renegade hog, farmer Stokes saddled a mule and visited a few of his neighbors to see if they had noticed a strange hog around their pens at feeding time.

The first one, rawboned old Zeb Butler, remembered the hog.

"Been two months ago, I reckon, when I first seen it. Big old sow hog. Sorta brownish with dark spots. Come here one morning and nearly ate up all the feed I throwed out. Been back lots o' times since. Ornery rascal. Mean and greedy. She's always gone when I go back to look. If you know who she belongs to, tell him to keep her up. I ain't standing for no outlaw hog coming and eating up all my good feed like this. I'm gonna shoot that sow if she keeps it up."

The next three farmers vaguely recalled seeing the hog. Apparently it didn't visit them regularly. But over on the far side of the valley at the Petticord Blalock farm, Stokes' inquiry brought old man Blalock raving to his feet.

"She's a slick one," he thundered. "Can't get enough to eat. She's here about every evening when I feed my hogs. Don't know where she comes from or where she goes off to, but feeding time is about the only time I ever see her. By this fall she oughta be fattened into prime butchering shape. I figger I got a good claim on her, feeding her like I been."

Stokes told Blalock his experiences with the hog and the old man was astounded. They agreed the brindle hog was, by design, getting its morning meals with Stokes and its evening meals with Blalock. "If we get too hard on it, it'll probably switch to somebody else's farm," Blalock said.

Stokes returned to the Blalock farm late that afternoon to watch the feeding. Sure enough, there was the same brindle hog fighting savagely to gobble up most of the feed.

He drew Blalock aside. "Come over to my house early tomorrow morning and bring your boys. We'll hide out around there and see where she goes. No use trying it here because she'll get away in the dark." Blalock agreed.

The hogs finished eating and the brindle hog stood looking at the men silently. After a few minutes, Stokes walked to his mule with Blalock following. Their attention had been shifted from the hog pen only momentarily. Stokes lighted his lantern.

"Check the pen now and see if the sow's there," he said. Blalock did and hollered: "She's gone. Already gone just that quick!"

Stokes had ridden half a mile toward home when his mule's ears thrust forward and the animal snorted in surprise. In a few yards more, he overtook a shadowy figure ambling along the trail. When he came abreast of the figure, he stopped his mule and lowered his lantern and looked into a face he knew he would see – the wrinkled, snarling face of Rennie Coble. Her eyes blazed from deeply sunken sockets. Her nose, long and plunging, might have been a beak. When her lips parted, the light revealed snaggy teeth.

"What on earth you doing out here by yourself at night like this Miss Rennie?" Stokes asked.

"None of your business what I do," she snapped at him.

"Well, I'm going close by your place. You can ride back of the saddle here on the mule if you want."

She ignored him. "Get out of my way," she spat.

Stokes kicked his mule into a trot. Soon he passed near the Rennie Coble cabin, half-hidden even in daylight, in a stand of field pines. She had lived here alone as far back as anyone could remember. Her irascibility and peculiar ways made visitors a rarity. She had no income that anybody knew of, no visible means of support. Come to think of it, she didn't keep chickens, pigs, not even a cow. Nor did she tend a garden.

Shortly after dawn next day, Stokes' two sons and Blalock and his two grown boys were concealed in a wide semi-circle out from the hog pens away from the Stokes dwelling. Stokes fed his hogs as usual and watched the brindle hog attack the food with customary gusto.

As soon as the hogs were finished, they went out to begin their day-long foraging in the fields and woods. The brindle hog angled off toward the spring. In that direction one of the Blalock boys lay hidden behind a brush pile. When the brindle hog got near enough to spot him, it broke into a fast trot, then loped up across the hillside toward the woods.

The Blalock boy exposed himself and gave pursuit to keep the hog in sight. But the hog appeared to be gaining headway. The chase led onto a beaten cow trail twisting sharply through woods and thickets. The boy was within a few yards of the grunting hog when it went out of sight around a sharp corner and into some bushes. The boy rounded the corner full speed when he collided head-on with Rennie Coble, who, obviously was headed in the opposite direction. Both sprawled on the ground and lay there stunned.

By this time, the other men arrived. They helped the sputtering, malevolent old woman to her feet. Gingerly, she tested her feet and arms and legs to see if they functioned. And all the while she muttered dark condemnation at the unfortunate boy who had caused her to tumble. Satisfied that she had no broken bones, she started to leave, but Stokes asked her to wait.

"You ought to be home in bed sleeping, Miss Rennie. How come you stirring way out here in the woods this early?"

"None of your business what I do," she snarled, hiding her face in the bonnet. She started to leave but Stokes stepped in her way again.

"This boy here was chasing a big brindle hog along that path when he run into you. You couldn't have missed it. Did you see any hog?"

She ignored him, jerked her shawl about her scrawny shoulders, tightened the bonnet on her head, and walked away.

"She's a blamed witch," Blalock said. "She's bewitched that hog some way I bet." Blalock and his boys departed.

Stokes found repulsive the idea crystallizing in his head. It turned his insides clammy to think of it. His mind didn't want to acknowledge it. Yet evidence indicated he was right.

Next morning the brindle hog did not appear at the Stokes hog pen. It figured into his theory. Stokes believed that the events of the previous morning had frightened the hog away from his farm, perhaps permanently. Later, one of the Blalock boys rode up on a mule with word from his father that the hog had not showed up at their place the evening before.

"It's probably switched to some other farm to eat," Stokes said to the boy. "Tell your daddy to ask some of his neighbors to watch for it and let us know."

Two mornings later, Stokes heard the roar of a long-barreled gun come from across the hill to the south, likely from the Zeb Butler farm. Following the sound came the faint squealing of a wounded animal. Had Butler shot the brindle hog as he once threatened to do? Stokes had to find out. At the brow of the hill, he met a panting, blowing Butler carrying his squirrel gun. Anxiety and fear showed in his flushed face.

"Thet old devil of an outlaw hog showed up yesterday and again a while ago," he gasped, his chest heaving. "We tried to hem her up and catch her this morning. But she wheeled and run. I grabbed my gun and shot her. She squealed something terrible. And I'm telling you it didn't sound like no hog squealing, either. I hit her in the front part. Looked like the ball tore off one of her front feet the best I could tell. She's bleeding bad. We can trail her by the blood. I told the boys to get started on the trail with the dogs and wait for us. Let's go."

The blood spatters were easy to follow. They led through the woods, across the wagon road, over a plowed field, and into more woods. Stokes knew the trail was leading straight toward Rennie Coble's shack. In a soft plowed field, he noticed the tracks were hog's tracks. But later the leaves and overgrown fields did not produce any distinguishable tracks. Once in the center of the woods, the dogs halted in confusion for a moment as if the scent had abruptly changed.

The trail of blood led through an open window of Rennie Coble's cabin. "I'll go through here and you boys come in the door," Stokes said.

He stepped through the window into the musty room, lighted by the sunshine from outside. He saw blood spots on the floor leading up to the bed. In the bed lay Rennie Coble with only her wrinkled face showing from under a moldy quilt. Blalock and his sons entered and stood at the foot of the bed.

In a whining voice, the old woman screamed at the men to get out of her house and leave her alone. More hideous than ever, her face looked strained and wan. It jerked and twisted as though she suffered severe pain. Not once did the covers descend lower than her chin. She flinched and cringed as Stokes bent over the bedside.

"How long you been in bed here like this, Miss Rennie?"

She howled at him to go away.

"We saw some blood and we think you're hurt and we want to help you. You've got to let us see where you're hurt so we'll know what to do. You may bleed to death here soon if you don't let us help you."

Still, she screamed at them to leave.

"Miss Rennie, we want to help you but you won't let us. We could probably save your life if you'd let us see what's wrong and do something about it. You're gonna bleed to death and die right here in this bed. I hate to see you do that. But if you won't let us help you there's nothing more we can do, so we're gonna be on our way. Since we won't ever see you alive again, Miss Rennie, I want you to shake hands with me before I leave."

Stokes stuck his right hand down toward the bed.

Impulsively, the woman's arm jerked under the covers and her right hand rose to meet Stokes'. Not until the hand was well exposed did she realize her mistake. Then her features contorted in rage at being so cleverly tricked. Then her face loosened, her head lolled to one side, and she lapsed into deep sleep.

They all looked at the exposed hand with shock and disbelief.

It wasn't a hand at all but a bloody stub of an arm, the end of which appeared to have been violently torn off, as if by a heavy slug from a long-barreled gun.

"I shot a hog, but I killed a woman," Zeb Butler mumbled to himself.

THE UNSHAKABLE LIZARD

Jenny, a young married woman expecting her first child a few months hence, looked up from her work in the yard of her Uwharrie home and saw an ugly, scaly brown lizard staring at her from the sunny side of a boulder. Try as she would, Jenny could hardly take her eyes from the short and sickening reptile. It sat there gulping steadily, imprisoning her in a hypnotic spell. She felt an evil influence creeping from the squat creature like a smothering hand gripping her entire body. Only with strong-willed effort could she turn her head to break the trance and walk away.

From the first encounter, a morbid fascination developed between the two.

Afterward, the strange lizard began following Jenny. She saw it everywhere she went. It wasn't an illusion, for other people saw it, too. Each time the chilling bond between the two grew stronger and more overpowering.

In her more rational moments, Jenny realized there would come a time when she no longer could resist this terrifying creature and would succumb to its power. Then what?

She told her husband, father, brothers and sisters about the lizard. None could understand the effect it had on Jenny. Yet it was plain for them to see how abnormally upset she became at the sight of the thing.

At her request and encouragement they began seeking ways to destroy the lizard.

The menfolk threw rocks and other objects at it. Early in the battle, which continued through the summer, one of Jenny's brothers threw a rock that lopped off a portion of the lizard's tail, making future identification positive.

Often the creature would crawl through the crack under the door of the cabin and appear inside the room. Irresistibly, Jenny's head would be drawn toward it, and she screamed or gasped at the sight.

Thereupon the men eased down their long-barreled rifles, took aim and blasted away. But when the smoke cleared, the lizard sat staring stonily and defiantly at them. They shot at the lizard so often that the bottom of the door became splintered from the fusillade.

Knowledge of the indestructible lizard grew. People came from great distances to see it.

One who came was mysterious old lady Dutcher who saw the effect the lizard had on Jenny and cackled in fiendish delight. The wrinkled old hag's attitude puzzled everyone.

If a witch existed in the community, and most people agreed one did, the unanimous choice for the honors was old lady Dutcher. Vile-tongued, slight and vehement, she lived alone, acted and looked the part.

A couple months earlier, Luke Springer had gone out to his hog pen one morning and watched with shock as an old sow and her litter of six weaning pigs, one by one, squealed sharply, reared and fell over dead. Luke swore a witch had cursed them with a death spell.

About the same thing had happened at Mint Calloway's home. Mint was standing at his barn when his cows came up from their evening grazing. One heifer reached the shadow of the barn when she snorted, reared pawing, and collapsed. Mint, too, convinced himself a witch's magic caused the heifer's death.

Jenny's father pondered these incidents and others and concluded that the lizard dogged his daughter because of a spell cast upon her by a witch.

Meanwhile, the problem of the tenacious lizard became an agony for Jenny, now spiritless and exhausted. "It leaves me so tired and sick I don't want to ever move again," she lamented .

In the last month of the lizard's spell, the family had to watch Jenny closely lest the lizard's hypnotic power make her follow it helplessly away from the house and into the forest to meet a doom they could only guess at. Once or twice the menfolk had to restrain her and forcefully return her to the house when they found her being pulled into the woods completely at the mercy of the lizard's spell. Her husband and the womenfolk had to guard against her leaving the house at night.

Not only did Jenny see the lizard at home, she also saw it at places she visited. Once, she came out of the country church after the long Sunday morning services to meet the lizard on the steps staring at her. She fainted dead away and had to be removed before she revived.

There was something sinister and supernatural about the lizard as it sat showing no other movement except the rapid inflating and deflating under its throat. If there was ever any attempt at communication between the two, Jenny was unaware of it, although she became so hysterical and frustrated at the lizard she screamed at it to go away and shouted for it to make known what it wanted.

Jenny's father had tried all but one last idea for the destruction of the lizard. All his life he had heard that a silver bullet would kill any witch or supernatural being. In his blacksmith shop, he melted a silver coin, poured a bullet and loaded it in his old musket. He kept the gun handy and waited.

Two days later the lizard appeared before Jenny outside the house. Her father crept inside for his musket, came back and drew a sharp bead at close range. The old gun roared. The silver bullet struck the lizard and knocked it through the air. It fell kicking, grew still and lay dead, its white belly glistening in the sun.

When Jenny came up and saw the dead lizard, she collapsed with relief.

The lizard was killed by the silver bullet at 2 o'clock in the afternoon.

Only a couple of hours later, Jenny's family was informed by a passerby that old lady Dutcher, who lived in a gaunt old house on a knoll back off the main wagon road, was having an attack of acute pain and was seemingly at the point of death. A delegation from Jenny's household went to see if they could help her. They found her moaning and groveling on her bed, crying that she was breaking apart inside.

"My heart hurts," she shrieked again and again as she clutched at her breast.

They asked her when her travail began.

"It came on me right at 2 o'clock," she wailed.

Then her eyes focused and she recognized her benefactors and shouted for them to get out and leave her be.

Months passed before she recovered from her sudden and unexplained attack. And afterward her powers of witchery were gone forever, people said.

No one doubted that she was the witch who cast the evil spell upon Jenny, and from that day to this, the lizard has been an object of aversion in the Uwharries, especially to women.

THE BIG BLACK BEAST

The old woman lived alone in a dreary house at Tuckertown, a mill village that once clung to the hillside above the Yadkin River in the wildest part of the Uwharries. She had little to do with her few neighbors, and her eccentricities were many and inexplicable. She flayed with her vile tongue anyone who met her displeasure, heaping curses upon them. So many who crossed her met with bad luck that people began to call her the witch of Tuckertown.

Where she came from and how she acquired her powers of witchery no one knew. She attached herself to the old house like a leech and no one could pry her loose – not even the owner, who soon quit trying; the place was worthless anyway.

The wrinkled old woman always wore bulky shawls and long-flowing dresses. She could be seen busily hobbling around her house, going to and from the forest, digging in her garden where she raised herbs and unusual plants. She foraged for wild berries, fruits and nuts. Neighbors who missed garden produce or found corners sliced off a side of meat in the smokehouse often complained that the witch had made an unseen visit.

Visitors to the witch's home were a rarity, indeed. The few intrepid souls who did venture there were almost always met with hostility. But they told of strange sights and activities. They said the witch dug odd holes in her yard and buried things. She boiled foul brew in a washpot from which rose clouds of oily smoke. She carried a lantern and prowled at night in search of spies. A yellow glow could be seen at an upstairs window long into the night. Folks often speculated about why she spent so much time in that room. But no one ever got inside to find out.

One afternoon a group of neighbor women walked by the sagging dwelling and heard groaning and moaning inside. They entered apprehensively and found the old woman on a bed in a room just off the front hallway. She appeared to be in terrible agony. The women asked repeatedly what was the matter, but the old woman gave no articulate answer, only groaning louder. The women offered her water and tried to make her comfortable before leaving, telling her they would return later to check on her.

About dusk the women returned, bringing their husbands and other villagers. The witch's condition seemed worse, and the women tried to get her to tell them what was hurting. Her answer came with screams of pain. With a glare, she ordered the visitors out of her house, even threatening to cast spells on them. But they could not leave her in such helpless condition.

Darkness fell and uneasiness spread like a fog throughout the house, sending a clammy chill through the visitors. A vigorous wind moaned in the treetops around the house and caused the puny lamplight to flicker, dart, and occasionally puff out. This brought a moment of panic until the lamp could be lighted again. The witch howled more terribly and frightfully than ever, went into racking spasms and knotted with pain.

Hamp Carter and another man sat at the bottom steps of the stairway which faced the open front door. To their left was the bedroom where the women tried to comfort the frantic woman on the bed. Outside, a few other villagers had gathered, attracted by the witch's cries, and they stood whispering in the pale light of a full moon rising over the trees.

Abruptly the wind stopped and the people outside the house grew still.

A hair-raising scream, this one of pure terror, tore from the witch's lips, and the women with her had to pin her arms and legs with the covers to control her thrashing.

Then silence. Cold foreboding silence. But only for a moment.

A loud resounding "clump" came from somewhere high inside the old house – like a heavy weight dropped on a hollow box.

The witch screamed again. It was a sharp scream of pain this time. The fear seemed to have left her. The women relaxed their grip on her and stared upward as if expecting the noise again.

It came again. Clump-ppp. Loudly. Then even louder, again and again.

By this time the two men at the foot of the stairs had risen and stood looking up into the blackness where the noise came from.

The clump-clump grew louder, faster, nearer. The men separated at the bottom of the stairs, backing away, expecting anything.

At that moment, Hamp Carter's two-year-old daughter, Malinda, toddled in the front door and stopped against the wall as if fascinated, too, by the expectancy spellbinding the others. A man started inside the house but stopped in the doorway holding high his lantern.

Into this circle of light now appeared a dark round object at the top of the stairs. It crashed to the bottom, sending the two men diving out of its way. For a moment, it paused, its waist-high mass pulsating and quivering, and two legless feet came into view, one resembling a bear's paw, the other a crocodile's spiny foot. The bulky object writhed with fantastic shapes and colors – an animal head here, a leg or wing there, an ear, an eye, a beak, a horn, a snout. These grotesque appendages popped in and out, hissing, growling, slurping. A strange, offensive odor filled the house. When the ugly mass began to move, revolving, other mismatched, monsterish feet appeared for balance, and the first pair vanished.

Malinda Carter had spotted her mother across the hallway, and in fear, she darted toward her – right into the path of the throbbing, monsterish mass. It knocked the child to the floor and rolled over her body, enveloping it. Her feet and legs vanished into it as it rolled to the door.

"Stop it! Stop it! It got my baby!" cried Hamp Carter. His wife screamed from the doorway and started for the mass.

The man at the doorway jumped aside, kicking at it. His foot stuck. He hopped along, flailed with his lantern as his leg was drawn inward.

"It's swallowing me! Help!" he screamed.

All the other men rushed up, beating on the hulk with sticks and rocks. But their puny onslaught was as nothing.

They caught their friend and tried to hold him, but they were no match for the force sucking him deeper inside. He screamed in anguish, pleading for help. Now he was in up to his knee.

"Amon, the torch! Quick, get the torch!" he shouted.

Amon lighted the rich pine torch in seconds, shoved it under the mass and held it.

Soon, the creature shuddered. The victim felt the suction easing. He jerked his foot loose and fell free. Then the beast emitted a horrible screech of pain and surprise and started rolling again, then bouncing out of the yard and into the forest, obviously hurt by the burns that branded it.

The men grouped with lights, guns, torches and dogs. They trailed the mass for miles in erratic patterns through the hills and woods, following skinned trees, crushed bushes, an odd assortment of tracks and a peculiar earthy scent. The trail ended at Cannan Creek, swollen by a recent freshet. Had the ponderous beast fallen in and drowned?

Whatever the answer, the men found no trace of little Malinda. The beast obviously had kept her.

Back at the witch's house, they found the old woman weak and exhausted but snoring peacefully on her bed. The women wiped sweat from her pallid face and left her slumbering under light covers. Gradually the witch recovered her strength and within a few days was her normal weird self. The parents of the missing child confronted her at every opportunity, pleading for an explanation of the black beast and asking if any hope remained for their daughter. The witch shook her head and said nothing. She died some years later and was committed to a grave in the loneliness of the river hills.

After the incident at the witch's home, Tuckertown became a ghost town. Fearing that something similar might happen to their children, most of the families moved away.

Malinda's mother died of grief. Bitterness fed the rage in the heart of Malinda's father. He was determined to annihilate the dead witch's black beast or die in the attempt.

In succeeding years, the story of the fearsome mass spread to every household in the Uwharries, gaining color and exaggeration as it went. It was said to devour wild game, fowl, dogs, cats, pigs, calves. Anytime anybody disappeared, especially a child, it was assumed that the beast got him or her. People whispered that it had to have a child about once a year to stay alive. And they believed that it assimilated the faculties of all the creatures it absorbed and could use them to assume the form of any other creature, enabling it to elude and confuse pursuers, as well as making it a formidable predator and threat to the safety of all.

Parents used the beast to frighten their children into quick obedience. Few people were brave enough to venture out alone after dark. Any disturbance was believed caused by the beast and the ghosts it spawned. Strangers passing through the community were suspect. So was any person or animal who departed from the norm, because some said the beast had power to inflict spells.

Hamp Carter investigated every report of the beast, bringing his dogs and guns, doing his best to stay on the trail, which always faded. Many adventurous young men joined Carter for a foray into the forests, hoping to glimpse the beast. Few of them stayed with the search for long.

Hamp and his occasional companions sighted the beast many times, even closed in to pump rifle slugs and shotgun volleys into it without effect. Once he emptied his gun into it, then clubbed it until it sucked his gun away. Other times it hardened its surface into an impenetrable shell and let him and his companions inflict whatever punishment they wished, their attacks doing no more damage than they might have inflicted upon a granite boulder.

Sometimes the searchers would pause beside a rock or stump to find it slowly come to life as the beast. It delighted in confounding them. It galloped off like a horse, flopped off like a huge bird, or slithered away like a python. When it developed the ferocity of a tiger and actually menaced him, Carter abandoned his pursuit until the beast cooled off.

One day Carter came to the chase prepared. After angering the beast with gunshots, he lighted the fuse to a dozen banded sticks of dynamite and tossed them on top of the hulk, which immediately sucked it inside. The resulting explosion blew parts of the beast all over the forest. Carter had won his vengeance.

After a year or so of beastlessness in the Uwharries, neighbors were shocked to hear cries of anguish coming from the old two-story home of Aunt Ila Bell, an aged widow who had lived alone 20 years. She had acted peculiarly since she claimed to have been bitten by the black beast several years previously. Now she lay writhing in agony in her downstairs bedroom, and it was all the neighbor women could do to keep her subdued. As their vigil with the sick woman continued into the night, there came a clumping high on the stairs and a shriek of pain from the bed. Past the lighted doorway came a large, black, round, heavy bulk, crashing through the closed front door and vanishing into the moaning wind of the winter night.

When Hamp Carter, an old man now, heard about this new black beast loose in the Uwharries, he said, "You know, several women claimed to me that they got bit by thet critter, but I never thought much about it until now."

STRANGE
HAPPENINGS

THE STONING
OF KING PHAROAH

One day in the fall of 1880, King Brooks, a 50-year-old farmer, walked to Sampson Hinson's barn to borrow his bull, King Pharoah. Brooks wanted to take Pharoah back to his farm and turn him loose to mate with his cows.

Farmers on both sides of the Yadkin River borrowed Pharoah for breeding purposes, for plowing, for pulling grain to the mill and logs from the woods. Just that morning, one of the Hinson women had used Pharoah to plow under some oats. Pharoah weighed nearly a ton, but he was docile and meek despite his vicious-looking horns. He often let children pet him, and he had never been known to harm anyone.

Only an hour or two earlier, Brooks had killed and dressed several hogs at his home and salted the meat away in the smokehouse. Now as he approached the barn he and his clothing smelled strongly of blood.

A big, rangy man, Brooks entered the pole fence, fastened a lead rope to the bull's halter and turned to lead him away. But Pharoah didn't follow. Apparently enraged by the smell of fresh blood, he charged, slamming into Brooks' back, knocking him against the fence. Pharoah's horns jabbed through the farmer's body again and again, long after all life had left it.

As Pharoah bellowed his anger, folks came running from the Hinson home, but they were too late to help. They found what looked like a big, ragged, red-stained doll impaled on the fence.

News of the goring traveled like wild fire through the river hills and within an hour the barn lot was filled with farm people who had left their wood cutting and grain sowing to view this ghastly thing that had once been a man. Unmasked hatred glittered in their eyes and dark muttering was heard as they watched the snorting, wild-eyed bull standing in a corner of the barn glowering and tossing its head.

The body of Brooks was scraped off the fence and later buried in the family plot a few miles upriver. After the funeral, people gathered to discuss the goring and what should be done about it. These people had been guided throughout their lives by Biblical teachings and they had been taught to find sanction in the Scriptures for their actions.

An elder stepped up and opened the Bible to the 21st chapter of Exodus and began reading at the 28th verse.

"If an ox gore a man or a woman, that they die; then the ox shall be surely stoned, and his flesh shall not be eaten; but the owner of the ox shall be quit.

"But if the ox were wont to push with his horns in time past, and it hath been testified to his owner, and he hath not kept him in, but that he had killed a man or a woman, the ox shall be stoned, and his owner also shall be put to death."

A group of indignant men demanded that Hinson release the bull for punishment. One version of the tale says that Hinson refused, even after they offered to pay for the animal. Thereupon they ignored Hinson and, like a determined lynching party, took possession of King Pharoah by force.

Many years later a descendant of Hinson said: "He would have taken the bull off and shot him himself if he had known what the mob intended doing with him."

At any rate, the mob, numbering nearly fifty men, subdued the raging bull with heavy chains and shackles. Pharoah resisted every inch of the way as straining mules dragged him along the wagon road, followed by men prodding with pitchforks and sharp tools. Finally, the mob secured Pharoah in a stout stable in the log barn of Arch Hinson nearly a mile away.

Then they gathered to hold counsel. One man raised a point.

"Moses laid down the law that if an ox killed a man or a woman, that ox should be stoned. But any fool knows Pharoah ain't no ox. – he begot about all the calves in this end of the county."

A pious oldster held forth.

"We must give him a trial," he said. "We must do better than the scriptures. We must give him a trial and then we'll know we're right."

So as the maddened bull struggled vainly to reduce the barn to shambles, the group held a trial.

Murphy McClendon, old and locally celebrated for his wisdom, was appointed judge by unanimous approval. He named a prosecutor and a jury and a man to defend the bull. All the appointees, the judge included, were ignorant and untutored in their duties. But it made no difference. No one had any knowledge of the laws of the land anyway.

The trial of old King Pharoah lasted most of the day and the arguments waxed long and loud. Chief evidence offered by the defense was that the law of Moses did not apply to the uncastrated Pharoah.

But the judge ruled that the law did apply. The jury, solidly opinionated, said guilty. "We recommend that the bull be put to death according to the scriptures," they said.

The crowd yelled approval. McClendon held up his hands. In one hand was the Bible, and he read the passage about the ox. "I sentence Pharoah, the bull, to be stoned until he is dead," the little judge shouted. He glanced at the sun low over the Uwharrie hills. "Tomorrow at high noon."

Men struck out for their remote farms to spread the news, and next morning every man for miles up and down the river was on hand.

The spot chosen for the stoning was a big oak tree beside the Big Lick road on a rocky hillside. A detail of men had gathered a huge pile of stones in readiness.

Meanwhile, the bull had turned into a raging monster. When the men went to get him shortly before noon, they had to climb up in the barn loft, lower heavy log chains over his head and draw it up high before they could control him.

Then old Alec, a former slave, went in the stable to shackle Pharoah's feet. Alec got too close and with a powerful lunge, the bull ripped a gash in his head. He jumped back cursing, his eyes blazing. "I'll get even with you for that, big boy," he promised.

Pharoah's head was chained down between his forelegs. His feet were shackled so closely that he could take only short steps. A dozen men manned guide chains on either side of his head in case he did try to break away. Six mules dragged him to the big oak where he was tied.

McClendon looked at his watch and raised his face to the noon-day sun. He opened his Bible and read: "And he shall be surely stoned..."

Baseball size stones battered the bull from every direction, thrown by a hundred men. They struck him again and again. Boys joined in. Women and children watched from afar. After an hour Pharoah was still on his feet. And the torture continued.

By mid-afternoon the bull had weakened and dropped to his knees. But his bellow still rang defiantly. Some of the executioners were tiring of the sport.

"Read the Scriptures again and see if it don't say to use something besides stones, Judge," someone suggested.

"It'll take to dark to kill 'im like this," another muttered.

"Look at 'im," a sweaty, overalled farmer said. "His ears is knocked off. His eyes is blinded. His face is ground into sausage meat. His hide is jelly. But he's still bellering at us and mocking us."

This was more than they had bargained for. It was an ordeal. Some of the men left. Others vomited at the sight of the bloody bull. The sun sank toward the trees.

"I'm leaving," the white-bearded judge said. "If you want to use anything besides stones on him, go to it, but remember, the Lord might not approve."

With the judge gone, the men brought out their pitchforks, knives and sharpened tools. They they plunged them into the bull's sides and back as other men kept pounding with stones.

Gradually the bloody, unrecognizable head of the animal sank lower. His great body shuddered. His knees collapsed slowly and he sprawled on his side. The men closed in.

But King Pharoah had not given up. His voice came again, long and resounding, mocking his tormentors. But his voice was the only life left in him now. The great strength was beaten.

Alec called a lull in the stoning. "Let me at him," he said.

Armed with a handspike, he went to the bull's immobile head and knocked off what remained of the long horn that had inflicted the scalp wound.

"Now I'm even with you, you big devil," he said.

But his lust for additional revenge surged and he brandished a sharp butchering knife and began carving hunks of dripping flesh from the side of the mutilated animal. He tossed the chunks to a pack of dogs which snarled and fought over the feast. While Pharoah opened his cavernous mouth, Alec carved and carved, his face frozen in vindictiveness.

And nobody had a mind to stop him.

When the crowd, dwindled now to a dozen, could stand it no longer, they stopped Alec, and someone took a muzzle loader and mercifully put a ball through the bull's brain.

The men had just enough time before darkness to drag the gruesome carcass to a gully and topple an embankment of earth over it.

In a lot of homes, sleep was evasive and uneasy that night.

Though there is nothing to substantiate it, tradition says many of the men who took part in the stoning met with bad luck and calamity later in their lives.

Until recent years there stood on the now abandoned Big Lick road a huge tree called the Bull Oak, which marked the spot where the stoning occurred.

Nearby was a mound of round stones which were said to have been used to kill Pharoah. They had been piled up as a monument to the valiant animal.

But the oak is gone now and the stones have long been scattered in the fields. The gully is under cultivation.

Some years ago, a woman in her 90's remembered that she was a young girl when the stoning occurred.

Each night for weeks afterward, she said, the cows and other livestock, which ran loose in the community, would gather at the spot where the bull was stoned and join in a mournful chorus of almost human-like wailing.

"It was enough to make the hair rise on your head," she said, "to hear all them cows up there grieving so for old King Pharoah."

CELIA EASLEY
AND OLD FREE HARRY

Celia Easley is a name that will bring a deep and nostalgic look in an oldtimer's eyes in the village of Cottonville. It will set little memory bells to tinkling in his mind.

It may take awhile to get his faculties geared to the subject, but then, if the weather's agreeable and he isn't offended by too many unwise interruptions, he may come forth with an amazing tale.

He doesn't know firsthand of what he tells, for the day of Celia Easley is far beyond the memory of anyone now living. "My mother loved to tell us children about old 'Aunt' Celia," he will begin. "And about her man that she bought, Old Free Harry."

"They owned all the property out this away," he'll say, waving his hand in a wide sweep east of the village. "Some 400 acres in all. Raised half a dozen kids or so. But old lady Celia died and the children ran through with everything."

The old man won't be content to let the story go in such meager fashion – not if you're willing to listen. He'll inject a lot of color, a bit of quaint dialogue, and just about make the characters of Celia Easley and Old Free Harry perform before your eyes.

And, most likely, he will stop and editorialize along the way.

A family of free blacks who farmed upon their own 400 acres amid the large slave population in the Uwharries in the mid-1800s was unusual. No other former slaves ever reached such prominence.

How did the husband and wife achieve their freedom?

By what means did they acquire such a large amount of prime farming land, more than many white farmers owned?

Cottonville was a trading center of some renown in that time, known then as Crossroads, where plantation masters came from all over the territory to examine the offerings of slave traders and the wares of vendors. It was the center of a large slave population known as the Black Belt, which was used to farm the fertile river land. Whites were relatively few in the area, but there was mingling of the races, and from this came Celia Easley.

The first documented evidence of her, recorded in 1833, lists her as being from Anson County. She purchased a 100-acre tract lying on both sides of Ugly Creek from Hich and Woodson Randle and Daniel Easley for $20. Evidently she was free at this time and had acquired money of her own.

Who owned her as a slave has not been determined, though it may be assumed from her name that it was an Easley, as a few families of this name were known to have lived in the vicinity. Her white father likely gave her freedom and showed her consideration while she remained on his plantation. Possibly he permitted her to work for hire to accumulate money of her own. Prior to his death, he may have willed or deeded land to Celia. But land was cheap then. It is quite possible that by thriftiness and industry, she bought all the land she later possessed.

Celia has been romanticized into a lovable character. She was said to be a gentle and affectionate woman, big-hearted, observant, and sensitive. She was young, free, and with opportunities that few blacks obtained in that day.

She began to hear wondrous tales of a young slave owned by William Randle, a big plantation master who lived miles away to the east near the Pee Dee River. The slave's name was Harry and he was said to be tall and massive. Celia obviously fell in love with the reports of Harry for she went to the Randle plantation for the purpose of buying him.

But the price was beyond her means, and in despair, Celia went back to toil in her fields for the money that would someday buy her Harry's freedom. She was young. She could work. She had faith that she could get whatever she cherished.

Eventually she did meet William Randle's price and Harry

became her own. She brought him back to her land as her husband. Folks are inclined to believe that there was some duly recorded legal notice of their marriage; at least something to show the skeptical white people who might challenge their rights.

Harry, who had the name of Randle, took his wife's name after the marriage and thereafter became known as "Old Free Harry" Easley.

Celia and Harry prospered. Their holdings became known far and wide. They started an orchard and were credited with originating a fine strain of apple trees. They opened up a spring used by travelers on the public trails. They farmed in peace and outdid many of their white neighbors.

Children were born to them and grew up unaware of the bonds of slavery or the early sufferings of their parents.

The official Stanly County census for the year 1850 lists Celia (spelled Selea) as being 47 years old, a mulatto, and a farmer. Her children, all listed as mulattoes, were: Sally, 19; Henry, 17; Judith, 14; David, 12; William, 10; and Elizabeth, five.

It is significant that Harry is omitted from the family census. Celia is listed as being the head of the family. Harry, it appears, was regarded as a slave and not as a member of the family.

Elderly people remember hearing their forefathers tell that after years of marriage, Harry's affection for his wife and benefactor cooled and at times he became unruly and abusive to her.

Aunt Celia's ardor for Harry also became less obvious with the passing years. An entry into the county register of deeds, (Book I, page 318) dated in 1846, brings to light the fact that Celia (again misspelled Seley) had become indebted to David K. McSwain for the sum of $36.76. Unable to pay the debt, she mortgaged her livestock, bed and furniture, cow and fodder, 200 acres of land on the west prong of Ugly Creek, and a male slave by the name of Harry. Evidently Celia had no compunctions about mortgaging Harry to appease her debtors. Perhaps it served to keep Harry in line, as well.

Later she paid off the debt, saving Harry from slavery again.

The "pattyrollers," white men invested with the authority to apprehend stray slaves as well as to keep whites in line, visited the Easley home one day and inquired if Harry had a pass. It was customary for a slave away from his owner to have a written pass or permission to be away. Apparently the white men were not acquainted with Harry and Celia, for they insisted that Harry produce a pass. Harry told them he was at his own home and didn't need a pass.

But the men insisted. Harry told them to go away and not molest him. Still they advanced as if to overcome him. Harry, possessor of a fitful temper, got riled, ran into the house and came out brandishing a long-barreled musket at his antagonists. Reluctantly they mounted their horses and rode away. Harry, so filled with wrath and indignation, swung his gun with such force that the barrel wrapped around a sapling in the yard.

Years passed and Aunt Celia, the stalwart mother and benefactor to many, died in the mid-1850's and was buried on her land. Her children became the heirs of all her property and possessions including their father, Old Harry. Valuing not the sense of freedom and fierce independence which motivated their mother, the children misappropriated their inheritance and became heavily indebted to white people in the community.

One by one, over a period of a few years, they mortgaged off "a tract of land whereon Celia Easley lived and died, and also all their undivided interest in Harry, a slave belonging to the heirs of law of Celia. decst., and also all of their personal property of every description whatever."

Eventually the mortgages were foreclosed and most of Celia Easley's lands fell into the hands of others. However, Old Free Harry was saved from slavery again, perhaps by the end of the Civil War. He lived with his son, Bill, who had managed to retain a fragment of his mother's lands. Bill, who was married and had a family, built his father a little cabin near his home and there Old Harry lived out the remainder of his days.

The Easley children became well known. Some of them eventually migrated to distant places. Bill Easley is remembered as having split 500 rails in one day, considered a noteworthy accomplishment.

Judith Easley was the most respected of the children. She married Frank Davis and was said to be the most like her mother of any of the children.

Johnny Davis of Stanly County is the son of Judith and a grandson of Aunt Celia. He remembers much of the story as it was told him by his mother. Few of the known grandchildren of Celia are alive today. Still fewer know the dramatic story of their forebears.

Today, the lands along Ugly Creek east of Cottonville are still referred to as the old Celia Easley lands. Until in recent years there was a fine spring of cold water near enough for Sunday church-goers to quench their thirst. It was called the "Old Harry" Spring. It is now forgotten and untended.

There is today, an old marshy pond down near Ugly Creek that is known as "Old Harry's Pond." It remains about the only reminder, save hazy memories, of this remarkable pair.

THRASH DOCTOR

Sixteen years after the close of the Civil War, a six-year-old lad played with his young friends in the snow at a home in the Stanly County section of the Uwharries. His aunt appeared in the doorway of the log house.

"John," she called.

The skinny boy left his playmates and walked to her. "Come inside," she told him. She told the others to go on playing, that John would be inside for awhile.

She led him into a warm room where a fretful young baby lay swaddled on the bed. "My baby's mouth is dreadful sore, John," she said. "Nothing we've tried has helped and the weather's so rough we can't get anyone to come and doctor it. I want you to try it."

Her words thoroughly alarmed him. How could he, a six-year-old, help the baby?

"John, old folks say that a person who has never seen their father will make a good thrash doctor. You never saw your father. Something's got to be done or the baby will die. I want you to try it."

He wanted to run. He told his aunt his mother was expecting him home right now. But his anxieties were quieted and she led him to where the baby lay. "Bend over him close and do as I tell you," she said.

John did as he was bidden. It was simple. He merely blew his breath into the baby's sore mouth. He wondered what good that would do.

Three days later he was told that the baby's mouth was well.

The incident did not go unnoticed in the community. "Son," the folks told him, "you're into it for the balance of your days."

And so he was. For the next 75 years John Huneycutt blew his breath into sore mouths with satisfactory results, a treatment commonly called "using." He was well up in his eighties when he died. In his latter years, he didn't go making calls on horseback or by buggy all over the country as he once did, although he still handled "patients" as long as he was able.

"I've had as many as three here in one day," he once said. His voice had a pleasant twang and his eyes were as friendly as blue skies to a fog-bound traveler. "They come from a wide territory around here."

Did he ever fail to cure a sore mouth?

"In all the years I've been at it, I've never failed yet that I know about. Some I've had to use for the second time, though, but they always got well."

"You wonder what it is I do to the child. Well, I just blow my breath into the baby's open mouth three times for three times. They started me off waiting an hour between times but I cut that down to half an hour. Saves time and works just as good."

Thrash was the local name for the fungal disease called thrush. There were two kinds of thrash, according to John: white and yellow. The former breaks out in a coat of white on the tongue and inside of the mouth, he explained, while the latter is distinguished by yellow blisters. He recalled "using" for both types on the same person.

Lots of times he'd be busy working in the fields when parents brought a sick baby to his home. But he stopped his work and "used" for it. Then, he'd go back to his work and have his wife call him at the next two half-hour intervals .

"I couldn't turn any of them down when they come like that," he said, then laughed. "I'll bet I've been hindered from my work long enough to have made a thousand dollars."

Scores of times people have come after him to treat sick babies that could not be brought out into the foul weather. He remembers one such trip.

"It was cold and snowing that day. We rode in a buggy all the way over across the river. I went inside and the womenfolks were sitting around the room with the baby. Another one was getting dinner ready in the kitchen. They began asking me questions. 'How long you been using for the thrash?' the baby's mother asked me. I told her since I was six.

"She began to bundle up the baby. 'You'll be wanting to take him out to the barn, won't you?' she asked. I told her I didn't have to take them to the barn. 'Why?' she asked. I told her I never saw my father.

"Other thrash doctors took babies to the barn and drew straws through their mouths and said words from the Bible. She thought I would do this. But me, never having seen my father, made a difference. She seemed satisfied then.

"Well, I went ahead and used for the baby. It had a real bad mouth. When I left I told them if it didn't get well to send for me and I'd use for it again. A few days later I saw the baby's father and asked him about it. He said it was well and there was nothing more wrong with the child."

Such cases were duplicated scores of times in his three-quarters of a century as a thrash doctor.

Skeptics? There have been plenty.

When an almost miraculous cure would be effected, the skeptic would say: "It was ready to get well anyway. John's treatment had nothing to do with it."

But the barbs did little to discourage the practice. John said there have been hundreds of happy parents who never questioned his methods.

When he was almost a grown man, John went back to school for a month. During morning recess one day, a woman came with her little girl and said she was looking for the "doctor." John looked at the girl's mouth. "Looked awful," he recalled. "The stuff had eaten her mouth and gums up until her teeth were loose. Her mother said she hadn't eaten in days." He used for her. She came back twice more and the teacher excused his "doctor" student to treat his "patient." Two days later the report came that the girl was well enough to eat and chew her food.

One time he thought he had failed. He used for a little boy's mouth twice and still his parents brought him back. His mouth looked worse instead of better. John noticed a rag around the boy's thumb. Removing it, he saw the thrash disease there. So he used for the thumb as well as the mouth and the boy got well.

There was a similar case where a child sucked two fingers on one hand. John used for the fingers as well as the mouth and the thrash cleared up.

There was one mysterious thing about it, though. John said he could never cure his own children of the thrash. Other thrash doctors reported the same limitations. So he swapped cures with another old thrash doctor in the area. He used for her infected children and she used for his own. He could, however, cure his grandchildren of the thrash.

John was just as mystified as anyone about his ability to heal the thrash. He claimed no supernatural power. He asked a medical doctor about it one time long ago. "You get it from a power higher than man," the doctor told him. "I have no medicine to cure it, yet you cure it without any medicine."

In many instances, John said he came right behind the doctor and cured cases where the doctor failed. In fact, when the early medical doctor in that section encountered a severe case of thrash, he would tell the folks to send for John, that he could cure it.

He remembers using for five sets of twins, three from the same family. One 84-year-old man requested his services and his sore mouth cleared up after John's treatment.

On one call in Union County, John asked the folks if they didn't have someone they could train for the job. He was getting too old to go gallivanting on calls that far from home, he told them. He explained the way he got started. They said they knew of a young boy who had never seen his father and that he might be a prospect.

"They must've got him doing it, too," John said with a laugh, "for I've never had a call from that community since."

In modern times, his practice slowed down considerably. But it never stopped. Until shortly before his death, people were still bringing their babies and young children with sore mouths and he was "using" for them with satisfying results.

Mothers for whom he "used" when they were babies brought their babies to him. "I tell folks I'm starting on the fourth generation," he said once.

He had little competition.

"There's a few folks around here who could do it if they would," he said. He knew of one or two people who, like himself, never saw their father. And this, apparently, is the most important qualification.

John's father was Tom Huneycutt, a Civil War veteran, who died a short while before John's birth.

"What'll we do when you're gone?" satisfied patrons used to ask him.

John's eyes crinkled and he smiled.

"Maybe there'll another one pop up," he told them.

THE LAST HERMIT

Any day now I'm still halfway expecting a contact from the "other side" where ghosts and spirits prowl. As the decades pass without it happening, I'm not disappointed. Because it still may come. And even if it doesn't, so what? If not to me, then maybe to someone else. For time, as we know it, is of no consequence in the spiritual realm.

Carlton H. Seeley made the transition from the physical to the spiritual world a few days before Christmas in 1970.

With him went a story he promised to give me - -a story involving a cataclysmic revelation he was destined to share with the world.

The last time I saw Seeley alive, six months or so before his death, he acted as if he thought the revelation and the sharing were imminent. I gave him my name, address and telephone number. He said he would contact me when he was ready.

I'm still waiting.

Carlton Seeley was the last genuine hermit of the Uwharries. The word "compatibility" must have been coined to salute Seeley and these unique hills.

A friend told me about the hermit and which twisty, unpaved road to take to find him.

"There's no driveway," he said. "Look for a big rock beside the road. If you have any females with you, you better holler first. He may not have any clothes on."

Traveling alone, I found the big rock, parked, slung a camera around my neck and started down a path through a straggle of oaks and pines. I stopped when I glimpsed his shack maybe 50 yards away.

"Mr. Seeley," I called. "Mr. Seeley...hello!"

No answer. So I moved closer. Then as I neared the shack, Mr. Seeley appeared around an outside corner and I stood face to face with the man who had become a legend in the Uwharries.

Though I had been forewarned about his appearance, I tensed, recoiled. He just grinned. I introduced myself and we began chatting.

Coarse matted white hair cascaded, almost in rivulets down around his head to tangle with his white beard, which reached on to his waist. Only his forehead, eyes, nose, cheeks and part of his mouth showed through that mass of wiry hair. A squirrel could nest in all that hair, I mused to myself.

The washed-out, threadbare overalls hanging on his six-foot frame were more than tattered. They had patches on top of patches. He wore a limp blue work shirt, the ends of the wrinkled collar pinned under his galluses. His dirty feet looked like tough leather.

His voice crackled out mellowly and sprightly, matching the glint in his eye.

He permitted me to look inside his two-room shack which lacked electricity and plumbing. He used rain and creek water, lamp and lantern light, plus a wood-burning heater for warmth.

The interior of his crumbling shack bulged with musty, spider-webby belongings – a bed, boxes, trunks, dresser, old organ, musical instruments, stacks and stacks of old magazines and newspapers. And books, books, books. The doors and windows were fragile with age. Cracks here and there let in air, rats and bugs.

A hundred feet further back in the woods stood a separate shack, which he called his kitchen, where he cooked on a wood-burning stove and ate his meals. Both structures were unbelievable in their pioneer crudeness, their dilapidation and isolation.

In between and off to one side, Seeley had carved a quarter-acre garden spot from the forest, which he spaded by hand and on which he grew vegetables organically. He was a strict vegetarian.

Even more unbelievable was the way he stored and preserved

his 1928 Model-A Ford which had brought him and all his worldly possessions into the Uwharries from his native Virginia in the late 1930's to settle on this 28 acres of backside-of-nowhere land for which he paid $100.

He just parked the Model-A in the woods and built his shack around it. The car wound up in a shed-like structure adjoining the rear of his shack. All I could see of the old car was the edge of the left front fender and part of the large headlamp. Years before, he had stored sawed slabs and firewood in, under, over and all around the vehicle. Eventually, the rotting wood effectively hid his car.

As a young man, Seeley said he worked in the automobile factories in Michigan until his health began failing. Then he headed south, working in apple orchards along the way. He said he was passing through the Uwharries on his way to Arkansas when his car broke down. The Uwharrie people were so neighborly about helping him get squared away that he decided to settle here for the rest of his life. As long as his health permitted, he did odd jobs for the farmers in the area and he worked some at a nearby flagstone quarry.

As a monotony breaker and to escape the torpor of the hot summer in the woods, Seeley went naked. He said it was healthy that way. He cautioned visitors to holler a warning if women and children were in the group.

Seeley told me he kept in perfect health. No aches or pains, no protesting bones or joints. Only rarely did he have a bad cold. He had not been hospitalized since coming to the Uwharries. He had good eyesight and hearing.

Unschooled, he taught himself to read and he could talk on many subjects with the precision of a college professor. Religion, philosophy and health were his favorite subjects. He could quote the Bible and passages from the great philosophers. He knew all about health and diet and natural and spontaneous healing processes. He coveted his Uwharrie isolation because it was highly conducive to reading, studying, contemplation, meditation, and prayer.

Seeley tuned in closely with nature and the supernatural. He seemed to have a sensitive sixth or seventh sense with which he could grasp knowledge and intelligence beyond the reach of most mortals.

He told me how he charmed or hypnotized a bird on his windowsill into complete immobility.

He indicated to me that he anticipated some sort of divine revelation which he would share with his fellow men throughout the world when the time was right.

So he kept waiting for his signals and signs to fall in place.

I was third on his list to get the story when he was ready. He had promised it first to two other newspapermen.

But time ran out for Mr. Seeley on that pre-Christmas morn in 1970. They found him barefoot and stiff in the snow outside his shanty where he had lived in solitude for 30 years.

Neighbors, a deputy sheriff and the county coroner who viewed the body said it appeared Seeley may have gone outside, possibly to get some firewood, and probably had a stroke or a sudden attack of some kind and couldn't get back inside.

Marks in the snow showed how he had made a vigorous struggle to crawl the few feet back to the safety of his door.

But he didn't make it.

The temperature that night was nine degrees.

A cousin in Orange, Va., claimed the body and took it back there for rites and burial. His age was figured at 88.

A savings account that few people knew about contained about enough money to pay his burial expenses.

A longtime neighbor was appointed administrator of his estate. All of Seeley's material possessions were auctioned off at a sale attracting hundreds.

For a long time, a few people had suspected something shady and unsavory in Seeley's past. But nothing ever surfaced in the official record to confirm this suspicion.

So far as I know, Seeley never took any writer into his confidence with an okay to print his complete story. Nor did he reveal the nature of his divine revelation. And up to now, he's shown no inclination to communicate with me from the other side.

THREE PLUCKED TURKEYS

Had it not been for a keg of spoiled wild cherry wine, the story of the three plucked turkeys, Moult, Poult, and Lem, would never have come out of the Uwharrie hills.

A family of Craigs lived in the hills along the Yadkin River and kept a few tame turkeys on their small farm.

As most families did, the Craigs also kept a keg of spirits on hand in the smokehouse for medicine and ceremonial purposes.

But something got into one keg of the wild cherry wine spoiling it, and Craig reluctantly poured it out in the edge of the field beside his home.

Three turkey hens, nearly grown, saw Craig dash out the wine and heard the liquid trickling on the ground. They wandered over to investigate, sipped the stuff and found they liked the taste. So they drank all the wine they could find, a considerable amount.

Soon the wine, which hadn't lost all of its alcohol content, took its effect and the turkeys keeled over unconscious one by one.

Feeding time came and the birds were missed. One of the Craig children found them lying motionless at the edge of the field.

The elder Craigs looked at the inert birds and figured they died from poisoning after guzzling too much of the soured wine.

Mrs. Craig, a stout homemaker who well knew the ways of the rough life on the isolated farm, sighed. She knew what she had to do. While the meat of the birds wouldn't do to eat because of the probability of contamination by the poison, there was nothing wrong with the luxurious feathers. Turkey feathers make soft pillows.

So she called her children and they set to work yanking out all the feathers on the three birds, which bore the pet names of Poult, Moult, and Lem.

Soon the birds were defeathered as clean as any chicken you buy ready for the pot at the supermarket.

"It's a pity to have to throw away such healthy fat-looking hens," Mrs. Craig sighed, shaking her head sadly. "A real pity."

But she ordered one of her boys to load the carcasses on the homemade wheelbarrow and dump them across the field in the edge of the woods near the creek.

During the rest of that day the turkey feathers were cleaned and prepared and stuffed into rough pillow slips and that night the family members slept with fluffy new pillows under their heads.

In the bright sunshine of the following day, one of the younger Craig boys was playing outside when he let out a terrified bellow so loud it reverberated through the woodlands like a clap of thunder.

His mother came running.

"Look, Maw!" the youngster yelled. "Whut is it?" He motioned a trembling hand toward the field.

And there, staggering and stumbling across the field came three of the strangest apparitions ever seen in that country.

It was Moult, Poult, and Lem, dragging their sore and stark naked bodies toward the house, squawking and pecking each other as they came.

Mrs. Craig nearly fainted. The family called everyone around to come look at the plucked turkeys. And nearly everybody came.

Much to the surprise of everyone, Poult, Moult and Lem survived the plucking. But until they grew another coat of feathers, they were the talk of the Uwharries.

WILD CHICKENS
OF THE UWHARRIES

In many ways I don't believe it still. But all I need do to prove it
to myself is drive to that old homeplace nestled in an isolated
Uwharries field. Always the proof's there. I've been back scores of
times since I first saw it, and it's right there.

That field was not always as vacant and grown-up as it is today.
From the time I could first walk, I visited often a clapboard home
there occupied by an old man and his three sons. The wife and
mother had died when the youngest son was a baby, so the boys
grew up in a womanless home.

We lived a mile away and I walked to the Merritt home as often
as I could during my boyhood. Always they were genuinely glad to
see me. They tutored me in the use of my single-shot .22 rifle and 12
gauge shotgun. They taught me to whittle and instructed me in the
ways of the wild animals and growing things. All of them were
heroes in my eyes because they praised my accomplishments and
took pride in my progress as a woodsman.

One of the boys learned to cook and he took over in the kitchen.
And he was good at it, the envy of housewives all around. He knew
just how to keep milk cool in the spring run, regulate cooking heat
in the fireplace, and mix the right amount of red pepper in his fer-
menting sauerkraut. The other boys farmed, sawmilled, cut
crossties and developed a fair apple orchard from which they sold
the surplus fruit.

Visitors were welcome at the Merritt home and hunters could

hunt in the Merritt woods. But old man Merritt and the boys were particular about one thing. They didn't want hunters or dogs disturbing their small covey of semi-domesticated quail which never strayed far from the premises. Bird hunters coming too close to the dwelling were asked to leave and hunt in the far reaches of the Merritt woods.

The Merritts called their quail "partridges."

They kept other fowl – chickens, guineas, turkeys and a few ducks – which, of course, the hunters didn't bother. But they prized their quail highly. The old man called them his wild chickens. Anytime of year, day or night, there always were a few quail around the Merritt home.

Hunters, aware that the tamer Merritt quail attracted other coveys, hunted as close as they dared to the homestead and they killed a lot of birds. But they worried the old man. Much as he hated to impinge on their fun, when their shooting got close enough to endanger his special covey, he never hesitated to ask the shooters to hunt elsewhere. This action caused some bitterness toward the old man, but not among those who knew him well. Pa said there were no finer people than old man Merritt and his sons, and I believed him. They were always gracious to me. Some people said the Merritts did a little moonshining back in the woods, too. I don't know. Maybe they did. Folks always felt sorry for them for being without a woman in the household.

When I got old enough to leave home, I was gone 15 years or longer before I had a chance to get back home long enough to look around much.

Old man Merritt had died and the sons had just drifted away. All that remained of the old place was the skeleton of the log barn, rising out of the weeds and broom sedge, and the scraggly remnants of the apple orchard.

As I tramped through the weeds looking for the ruins of the old dwelling, I flushed a small covey of quail. They whirred into flight and traveled only a short distance before settling again in the cover near the orchard. No longer was anyone left to protect the old man's wild chicken-partridges, I reflected. Hunters probably slaughtered them now.

On a frost-bleached morning late the next November, I returned to the Merritt place to go bird hunting, using an expert bird dog borrowed from my brother who lived in the community. Starr, the setter, flushed a couple of coveys and I got half my limit before we reached the Merritt place. There I knew we would find quail. I let Starr work up to them gradually. Soon, he went into a rigid point. When I gave him the signal to flush them, four big quail whirred up. I dropped two with a single shot. The other two settled not far away. These were nice quail, extra large and plump.

We circled and when the other two rose, I downed one. The remaining bird alighted in the tall weeds beside the orchard. We zeroed in on him and he rose, a beautiful target which only a novice could have missed.

I spent the night with my brother and next morning went bird hunting again with Starr at the Merritt place. Practically the same thing happened. Four birds arose. I killed one then and one each on three successive rises, none of them flying far away.

That afternoon – not more than four hours later – I came back to the same place and killed four more birds the same way. And then, I discovered I could do it anytime. I could come to the Merritt place anytime – half a dozen times a day if I wished – and flush and kill four fat quail. They made easy targets because they refused to fly far or fast.

It developed into a pattern. Even without Starr, I could approach from the same way, stop in the same spot, hoist my gun, and up would fly four quail. I'd get one and sometimes two on the first rise, then proceed to practically the same spots and knock off the other two or three. Like clockwork. Almost like skeet shooting. I almost wore a path around the orchard that first season.

Folks marvelled at my fantastic luck. Without a dog, even. I never told them about the incredible pattern, or about the inexhaustible supply of fat quail in foursomes, because they wouldn't have believed it. Even I found it difficult to believe.

I told my brother the territory I covered in my hunting and he tried it, but after hours of hunting, his luck was spotty and the few quail he brought back were inferior to mine.

After a couple of seasons of loading down the larder with fine quail and giving many to my friends, I became locally celebrated as a quail hunter extraordinaire – able to bag his limit within a short time, hunting solitary, without a dog, and taking each bird on the wing. Other hunters wanted to go with me, which I wouldn't permit. Neither would I ever reveal my methods. However, I know other hunters surreptitiously watched me from afar, then came to the same spot, with and without their best dogs. But their results were uniformly disappointing.

One day at the Merritt place I got the strangest feeling, a sensation I had experienced vaguely before while here. An itchy, irritable, uncomfortable feeling. Like critical eyes were watching me. But no one else was around. Only the quail. The quail? Yes, just the quail. Then it dawned on me. Eyes? Watching? Yes...yes! Eyes watching and disapproving.

I still go back to the old Merritt place several times a year. I never take a gun anymore.

I go to see if the partridges are still there. They always are. I have a feeling they always will be.

On my visits in recent years, the four quail have become quite tame and friendly. They waddle around my feet, completely unafraid. I sit down and lean against the rotten trunk of an apple tree. The four birds twitter and murmur. They perch on my legs, arms and shoulders. They look at me with familiar and expressive eyes.

Sort of like the old days when I was a kid and stopped here to visit with old man Merritt and his three sons.

A Fork In The Grave

A fork, a dare, and a pretty girl form the basis of a strange tale imbedded in Uwharries folklore.

The fork was an ordinary table fork. The dare was made as a jest by a group of merrymakers. The pretty girl took the dare just to prove she wasn't afraid of a journey alone in the dark night.

Two girls were spending Saturday night in the home of a third girl in the neighborhood. They had their parents' consent and everything was shaping up for a grand weekend. The visiting girls were to meet their families at church next day to go back home.

Early in the night, the girls held a party in the hostess' home. Some young men came. One played the banjo, and there was dancing and talking and lemonade drinking, the party properly chaperoned by the third girl's parents.

During the chit-chat, someone mentioned the fresh grave covered with new flowers at the church a mile away.

Someone else said, "I dare somebody to walk over there tonight and bring back a flower off that grave."

Somehow the attention shifted to Della, one of the two visiting girls. While Della appeared to be intrigued with the idea, she did not volunteer to make the trip.

"Instead of bringing a flower back," a boy suggested, "how about taking something from here and leaving it on the grave? Then, if we see it on our way to church in the morning, we will know, indeed, that she was there."

Still, Della did not agree.

But after the company had gone and the three girls were all bedded down, the other two girls kept daring Della to go to the new grave.

Finally, Della agreed. "But what will I take?" she asked.

"I'll get you a fork from the kitchen," said the girl who lived in the house. "You can stick it up in the grave and leave it and we'll bring it back home after church tomorrow."

While her friend went to get the fork, Della dressed. Fork in hand, she slipped out of the dark house.

The stars winked white and brittle in the midnight sky as Della walked briskly along the road toward the cemetery. She was too scared even to turn her head to look beside or behind her. Every sound made her wince. But she was determined to show the others. She would leave the fork plunged into the grave to prove she wasn't afraid.

Her heart beat faster and she hardly dared breathe as she came close to the new grave at the edge of the cemetery. But she walked to it, knelt down, and pushed back the flowers from the center of the mound of earth. She raised the fork high and plunged it down.

Still crouched beside the grave with the sweet odor of the wilted flowers in her nostrils, she decided to take a rose back with her just for good measure. She plucked one from a wreath.

Her mission finished, she stood up to walk back home. But as she turned, something tugged at her long dress...tugged and held fast.

Back at the house, two tired and sleepy girls grew weary of waiting for Della and fell asleep.

They awoke next morning and Della wasn't with them. Frantically, they ran to tell parents.

The warm sun was an hour high in the Sabbath sky when they found Della lying beside the new grave in the church cemetery, dead, a look of horror frozen on her young face. One pale hand still clutched a wilted rose.

Looking closely, they saw the edge of her dress had been pinned to the grave by the prongs of a fork.

WHEN THE UWHARRIES DANCED A JIG

The week-long revival at the country church was about over and so far it had been without success. The crowd, small and unresponsive, was a long way from being under a spirit of conviction. But the minister, full of hope and belief, was on his knees fervently praying that the unfeeling hearts of his listeners might be shook anew.

Abruptly, the empty benches up front began a jig dance and the oil lamps hanging on wires from the ceiling began swinging in wide arcs. Creaking and groaning, the entire building heaved and sighed upon its ancient foundation like a weary mule wallowing in the dust.

Pandemonium resulted. The heretofore drowsy congregation jumped to its feet in unison and bolted for the nearest door. Children were nearly trampled in the mad scramble. The minister, with a wild look of terror on his face, dived out the pulpit window.

The incident at this church typified what happened at many churches in the Uwharrie country in which services were in progress that August night.

From all over the countryside shouting and wailing arose in the sultry air. Horrified people wondered at this phenomenon. What could cause the very earth to pitch and quiver under their feet? Many thought the end of time was at hand.

When the shaken congregations reassembled in the churches that night, as well as following nights, the long suffering preachers were overjoyed at the responses and rededications to their appeals to make things right with the Maker.

Elsewhere throughout the the Uwharries as well as a large part of the Southland, people were equally frightened and baffled. Not many had experienced an earthquake before. The Big Quake of 1886 brought fear and trepidation and a spirit of contrition upon the people of the Uwharries the likes of which has never been seen again.

People stayed up most of the rest of the night, praying, trembling and making restitution. They looked askance at the omnipotence of the Almighty, feeling they had been given a taste of what the end of time might be like.

One woman who was in bed at the time said she counted 13 separate convulsions of the earth. Each time the dishes rattled in her kitchen.

At one sawmill camp the workmen had the steam whistle propped closed with a slat standing upon a rock in the ground. The quivering of the earth loosened the prop and allowed the whistle to shrill, piercing the night with its blast. It continued blowing until the head of steam was exhausted, and people within hearing were sure it was Gabriel's trumpet.

One old man who wasn't within sound of the whistle paced the floor nervously as the ground kept shaking. Finally, when he could bear the suspense no longer, he summoned a sharecropper who lived in a little house on his farm.

"Dakus," he whispered. "The world has come to an end I know."

"Has the trumpet blowed yet?" Dakus asked unperturbed.

"No," the older man replied, "but I'm expecting it just any minute now."

Dakus muttered foully under his breath, rubbed his sleepy eyes and returned to his bed in the cotton house determined to wait until he heard the trumpet before he made amends.

Another man, thinking the commotion caused by the quake was a marauder outside his house, went out and set free his newly acquired watch dog to chase off the prowlers. In his confusion, he neglected to unfasten the trace chain which was hitched to the brute's collar. The dog, having no sense of loyalty to his new owner and no compunctions about pious duties, seized the opportunity to head for his previous home. He lit out full speed across the fields with the trace chain clanking in his wake.

The dog's former owner was in his yard with members of his family praying in earnest supplication. Eager to get back home, the big dog attempted to jump a rail fence bordering the yard and the chain made a terrible clanging. The man of the house, hearing the clatter, fell over backward and groveled on the ground. "I know I've done wrong, Mister Devil," he wailed, "but you don't need to bring chains to fasten me up in. Take me like I am, Mister Devil, I'll go."

Near the mostly black community of Cottonville, frightened residents gathered at their church and filled the night air with chants and lamentations. A few whites hearing this unusual and unholy racket decided the noise was an uprising of former slaves. They barricaded their homes and broke out guns and ammunition.

During the quake, one man who had come into possession of a new pocketknife by unjust means hurled it through his open window trying to placate the tossing earth.

One back-country man on his way to town the morning after stopped by the wayside blacksmith shop and hollered to the smithy, "Did you hear where she fell in at?"

It was the theory of some that a portion of the earth's surface had fallen and hit "bottom" so hard it had caused the earth to bounce and roll.

Actually, the earthquake was centered around Charleston, S.C. where it did severe damage.

Following the quake, the Uwharries saw a season of sweet peace and charitableness characterized by many acts of brotherly love. Debts were paid. Stolen articles were returned mysteriously. Embittered persons were reconciled by the score.

An intense religious awakening reigned. Many churches continued revivals for weeks. Church memberships swelled and attendance set records.

As long as the tremors lasted, people walked circumspectly and were mindful of their neighbors. But when all signs of the violence passed and the earth continued its operation without any rough and tumble antics, the populace drifted back into old ruts. Vows and rededications brought by fear were soon forgotten.

But there were reminders of that hectic August night for many years afterward. In some sections, wells dried up. Springs which normally went bone dry in the summertime now brought forth cold water even in the hottest and driest of conditions. Other springs disappeared completely and new springs appeared. Small streams changed courses or disappeared into the cracked ground. Dislocated buildings and tumbled chimneys were a common sight.

The terror of that night of the Big Quake made an indelible impression. Some people went berserk. Others slept peacefully through the tumult. But all were made clearly aware of what can happen to the seemingly solid earth under their feet.

And to this day, nothing has happened to equal the time when the Uwharries danced a jig.

POWER OF THE PIPE

Many people around the Uwharries remember the tale about "Uncle Lucian's Light." Uncle Lucian was the uncle of one of my great uncles, Uncle Bill, who has been dead many years now. Uncle Lucian was out in the woods alone cutting cordwood one day when he looked up and saw this great shining light. Coming from it out of the sky was a hunk of solid material which slammed into a stump near his feet. Uncle Lucian was overwhelmed. He interpreted the light as a divine call to preach. And though he had a house full of children at the time, he started out preaching and continued to his dying day. Oldsters say his fiery sermons were of an unusually inspired caliber with the dominant theme being that God and goodness still will be revealed to people if they will but be quiet and seek them.

Little importance was attached to the hunk of metal that fell out of the sky at Uncle Lucian's feet. Not many people ever believed that part, anyway, so he stopped telling it. But he did take it home for his kids to play with. Everyone who had much to do with the stone benefited handsomely. All of Uncle Lucian's children became professional men and women. Even old Yelper, the hound who loved to sleep with his nose across the tarnished meteorite, developed into the best squirrel dog in three counties, and was the first dog to have a hundred people gather to mourn his passing. But, strangely, no one ever seemed to relate these benefits to the metal.

Many years later, Uncle Bill found the abandoned hunk of metal at Uncle Lucian's homeplace, brought it home with him and used it as a door stop and as ballast for the well bucket among other things. And even I can remember when people came from afar to carry off the cold, sweet water from the well, which they were convinced cured diverse ailments.

An inveterate whittler, Uncle Bill jabbed his knife into the hunk one day and saw it yield. There came the time when he took the hunk to the workbench and sawed off a chunk from the corner. The rest he placed in a crotch in the barn framing. From the smaller piece he whittled out a pipe bowl and stub of a stem. And the longer he whittled on it the sharper his pocketknife became.

Well, the use of the pipe evolved slowly, but they said from the very first time he smoked it you could sense a change in him. The pipe transformed him from a diffident tenant farmer into a versatile man who gained wide respect in his community. It gave him wisdom and wit and made him jolly and poetic. He was called on to make talks and people went out of their way to get his opinion on things. He even became a good singer, whereas he had never sung worth a hoot before.

My first introduction to the power of the pipe came one lazy spring day when rain ran us out of the cotton patch about mid-afternoon. After fooling around the house a bit, Uncle Bill, cousin Bennie, and I wandered out to the granary. Uncle Bill reached up in a cleft behind a rafter and got a glass jar and shook some trashy-looking stuff into the pipe and packed it with his finger. He looked at Bennie and me and walked out toward the barn. Bennie nodded at me and we followed.

We climbed up in the barn loft and settled down in the remnants of winter's hay with Uncle Bill a little ways in front. He had the pipe going now and presently a cloud of smoke rose underneath the tin roof on which the rain prattled. Bennie kept a finger across his lips and nodded for me to keep looking at the smoke. I was aware of the two mules, old Bess and young Bert, snorting in the stable below us.

A movement of light in the smoke caught my eye and from then on my attention never wavered. At first the light flickered like a TV set warming up, then a wide screen outlined itself in the fog and on this screen was light, movement, people, animals, and all sorts of action. I couldn't figure it out for a few minutes. While there seemed to be some sort of continuity to the action, I couldn't follow it. Then I stopped trying to fathom it. I just relaxed and let all my senses succumb to the wonderment on that screen. Then I caught on. Like a sort of rushing wind, it hit me and I understood.

The picture was about Indians and Pilgrims – how the Indians taught the newcomers to stalk game, trap wild turkeys, skin slain bears, dig for tender roots, catch fish, prepare and seed the land. When it was over, I was so enthralled, Uncle Bill had to nudge me and help me down from the loft and on to the house for supper.

That was the first of many such sessions in the barn loft with Uncle Bill's smokescreen pipe. Saturday afternoons, Sundays, rainy days, and lots of times after supper in the cool of the evening, we'd look at those smokescreen movies. Sometimes Aunt Jenny and the girls would join us; sometimes not. Whatever your troubles, that pipe cured them. Worry and want vanished. You could climb into the barn loft dead tired and emerge, after one of those sessions, fresh and invigorated in body and spirit.

Although you heard no sound, you understood, for all the noise, dialogue, and narration registered on your senses just as if you were hearing it. And there was no addiction or compulsion associated with the pipe movies. Come to think of it, I never remember thinking of the pipe except when time hung heavy. It affected Uncle Bill the same way. You never could activate the pipe if there was work or anything important to be done.

That pipe was better than any movie or TV you've ever seen. We learned to create and order up any kind of viewing we wanted just by dumping the right type of fuel in the firebox. Took a lot of experimenting to get new formulas worked out, but it was fun.

Plain old rabbit tobacco produced fuzzy, low grade, low budget westerns. Add a pinch of domestic tobacco and the quality improved. Corn silks and shucks, carefully dried and ground up, brought hilarious comedies out of the pipe. Dogwood blossoms, leaves and bark, dried and pulverized, produced superb religious movies and Biblical documentaries. Stuffing from an old horse collar mixed with dried snake skin and seeds from Aunt Jenny's red pepper brought excruciating drama and mystery to the screen. We lucked onto color by accident – with a combination of mulberry leaves, a crushed cardinal's nest, and dust from a rotted log.

Bennie and I kept experimenting with other ingredients and mixtures. Such things as spider webs, wasp nests, catalog pages, shavings, dust from the bottom of the woodbox behind the kitchen stove, bits of thread and scraps from the sewing basket, even wads of hair sheared off old Bess' mane. The results were hilarious, breathtaking, musical, upbuilding and never dull. We stored up cans and jars full of special ingredients and kept them hidden up in the eaves of the barn.

Then we discovered a new dimension in the pipe's personality. A frightening thing in a way. It started after Uncle Bill began letting a select few outsiders in on the pipe sessions, mostly neighbors and close relatives who visited. And since Uncle Bill, despite the cultural benefits the pipe brought him, remained a tenant farmer, he'd quarrel with the landlord after harvest and often go stomping off to find another landlord who'd give him a better deal, and a move would be in the offing. That's how the pipe became known in half a dozen communities all over half the county.

Gradually we learned if a person with something strong on his mind came into the presence of the pipe, when activated, the pipe would latch onto this dominant mental channel and begin showing educational pictures on this theme. There were some pretty eerie characters who found their way into the barn loft sessions. We saw some of the damnedest battles, ballgames, cockfights, poker games, hoboing, racing, pirating, racketeering, moonshining, preaching and woman-chasing you've ever seen or read about to this day. Included in them were lots of new ideas. Young as I was, I remember thinking that an awful lot of good for humanity was waiting to be unlocked in that pipe.

That's when Eustace Tolliver came along. A tall boy with a blocky face and slow-blinking eyes, Eustace was introduced to the power of the pipe through the influence of LouEllen, Bennie's older sister. LouEllen's eyes were possessive and hopeful when she looked at Eustace. But in Eustace's eyes were only stars. He was a bug about stars and everything up above and far away. Worshipped them. You could meet him walking along the road and he'd be spouting out names of stars and heavenly bodies. Madly moon crazy, people said of him. They said he nearly drove his teachers crazy with astronomical questions. Every clear night from a high treehouse in the woods near his home, he studied the stars through his homemade telescope.

It was just after dark on a cloudy night when Bennie and I lured Eustace to the barn loft on a nickel bribe each from LouEllen. LouEllen was waiting along with Uncle Bill, Aunt Jenny, and several of the neighbors. They had the pipe fired up and going strong. Since it operated on the choice of fuel when no one had anything strong on his mind, it was showing a cheap, vaudevillian comedy when Eustace settled down in the hay beside LouEllen.

Then a strange thing happened. For the first time, the pipe faltered. The pictures fluttered and flickered and jumped and blurred. It blacked out completely for a few seconds, then resumed – exquisitely happy, it seemed – and we were zipping along in inky blackness amid galaxies of big, bright stars and heavenly bodies. I looked at Eustace and he sat there enraptured.

That was the first of our many trips to and from outer space on the power of that pipe.

Naturally, Eustace became crazy about the pipe. A big nuisance at the pipe sessions, too, for the pipe beamed onto his star channel every time and zoomed us away on another space expedition. As new and exciting as these trips were, they became tiresome after a time to most of the barn loft viewers because they were on such a high level that nobody could understand their significance except Eustace.

But, boy, did he love them. Although he couldn't talk about the pipe, either, he'd come into the field where we were working and stand there and whimper and plead with his eyes. When Uncle Bill could stand it no longer, he'd give the pipe to Eustace for him to take to the barn loft and fire up himself. Which made him ecstatically happy. And as often as we could, Bennie and I and LouEllen, too, would sneak away and join him in the barn loft.

Eustace learned tricks with the pipe of which Uncle Bill was incapable. He learned how to guide and control the pipe with his mind. It was as if the pipe were a vehicle, which it literally was, and he the driver. For instance, we'd be about to bust in for a landing on the moon when Eustace would start concentrating on Mars and there we'd go streaking off to Mars, arriving in seconds, too.

We took low-altitude flights around Mars and Venus and Saturn and dozens more planets about as quickly and easily as a hot-rod-der can zoom around a city block. From galaxy to galaxy, universe to universe, we cruised the wondrous reaches of space on the power of that pipe. Trying to enumerate all my fragmentary recollections of those stunning sights is pointless here. For I was too immature then to add it all up. But one thing I do know. We saw life in those other worlds. Plenty of intelligent life and movement and mechanization and water and greenness. What's more, we felt the essence of each. Some were weird, chilling and evil; some warm, inviting and benevolent.

After Eustace and LouEllen were graduated from high school, Eustace enrolled in Founder's College at the other end of the county after the Rev. Brete Mundy browbeat old Gus Tolliver into letting his son enroll, with the preacher having to stand good for the tuition.

It was his drawings which created such a furor at Founder's. This shriveled-up college and faculty nearly went into orbit itself when Eustace began showing his drawings of space, which the power of the pipe permitted.

He'd collar old Dr. Herman Capoote, the president, and other professors and show them his penciled drawings of whatever planet or solar system, known or unknown, that had caught his fancy. They nearly institutionalized him and probably would have if old Gus and the Rev. Mundy had not intervened. Old Dr. Capoote nearly died from the notoriety leveled at the college after two newspaper guys heard about Eustace and printed a story about him and his disquieting drawings.

Well, it turned out that two nationally prominent astronomers from some exclusive-sounding observatory came and examined Eustace and his drawings and shook their heads hopelessly. Dr. Capoote shook his fist in Eustace's face and confiscated his heretical drawings and put them under lock and key, although I think he did send some of them to the Department of Defense to check as a matter concerning national security. Eustace grew moody after that and developed a distrust for pompous people, but he kept on drawing at home and studying stars.

World War II took him out of the college's hair and put him in the Army's. The night before he left, I sneaked out to the barn and found that forgotten chunk of pipe metal and sawed off a corner and gave it to Eustace early next morning without anyone knowing. It was big enough to make a pipe out of, yet small enough to carry in his pocket. You may have read about the intrepid Pfc., Cpl, Sgt. and Lt. Eustace Tolliver and his fabulous fighting record. He and his company were decorated and commended a dozen times. He told LouEllen about some of it in his letters. Then, in the taking of Berlin, came the cryptic message, "Missing in Action." Later, he was presumed dead.

Although Uncle Bill moved a time or two during the war, he had faithful viewers for his pipe sessions which were held several nights a week the year around. Since the war was on everyone's mind, the pipe showed war pictures. Old Gus may have seen Eustace hurt or captured in one of these, I don't know, but we remember his face broken and tragic one day. I didn't get to see many of these sessions because the adults figured these war pictures were too gruesome for us kids.

I'm not saying that pipe had anything to do with bringing the war to a close, but you will remember that late in the war there was a powerful lot of praying for peace going on. The same thing happened in our community. A few of our people with unshakable faith in prayer came into the presence of the pipe. In some unfathomable way, the pipe may have responded and hastened the end.

The end of the war saw the end of the pipe, too. It happened one evening when one of the viewers got careless and flipped a lighted match down into a pile of straw. Absorbed with the pictures, the viewers didn't know about the fire until flames had devoured half the barn. In the rush to get down the ladder, someone knocked the pipe from Uncle Bill's hand and it fell into the inferno. They just had time to rip some boards off the backside of the stables and get the two mules out when the old structure collapsed and everything burned to ash.

By daylight next morning every available person who had ever witnessed the power of the pipe was at the scene with rakes and shovels and sacks and tubs and boxes. All day long they raked and poked and sifted. Some carted away quantities of the ashes and rubble while others carefully sifted it through fine mesh wire. There was no talking about what they were doing. And many were the outsiders who came and marveled at this strange and silent group which worked so steadfastly at its task and remained so uniformly unresponsive to questions. They cleaned up everything right down into the topsoil, but they didn't find the pipe.

Later, the barn on the farm where Uncle Bill had lived last burned, and again the same silent group came and poked and sifted and carted away the ruins. But they didn't find anything. In the next few years every barn on every farm Uncle Bill was known to have lived burned and the silent legion came and minutely examined the ruins.

The county fast gained notoriety for its ghouls who never could tell what they were looking for. But of course I knew and the other members of this legion knew. They were looking for that pipe of Uncle Bill's. And though it's ghastly to contemplate, I suspect some barns have burned just so there'd be fresh ruins for these ghouls to sift through. People became aroused and suspicious and there were dark whispers to the law. Along then was when reporters began referring to the pipe-seekers as the "Ruin-Raking Ghouls of Stanly County." You may remember reading some of the write-ups in the newspapers and magazines. But these writers really didn't know the half of it.

Uncle Bill didn't live but a year or two after the pipe disappeared. He never could adjust and just wilted away. His last strength was spent re-visiting old barn sites where he had lived in vain hope of locating a fragment of the pipe or a piece of the larger hunk. In his last few weeks he sat out in the yard in the cool of the evening, a sorrowful figure, and there was a great loneliness and unfulfilled longing tugging at his eyes as he stared into the sunset.

Eustace? No other word ever came about him and everyone presumed him dead. LouEllen married another of her girlhood sweethearts and had five kids in 10 years.

But I've got a different idea about Eustace. I believe that boy's still alive and studying stars, maybe even out there with the stars themselves, transported there by the piece of the pipe I gave him before he went off to the war.

THE MULE EGG

Back in the 1930's two Northerners bought a homestead in the middle of the Uwharries and set about equipping it for what they thought would be the idyllic life of farming. Everybody told them they had to have at least one mule on the farm for plowing. Hearing about a farmer some miles away who had a mule for sale, they got in their pickup and drove off to buy it.

Unfortunately, the owner had sold the mule just before they arrived. Quickly sizing up the strangers as greenhorns, the wily trader knew he could sell them something anyway.

He nodded toward a large, orange pumpkin near the barn.

"That's a mule egg about ready to hatch," he said. "I can sell you the mule egg for the same price I got for the mule."

The strangers found this agreeable, paid him, loaded the mule egg into the rear of the pickup truck and set out for home. Along the isolated road, the truck hit some bumps, causing the mule egg to bounce off. It fell on a big rock beside the road and burst open, scattering pith, pulp and seeds everywhere.

Right at the point where the mule egg burst open, a big, bedded, cottontail rabbit could stand the excitement no longer. He jumped up and streaked down the side of the road, then off into the woods as only a scared rabbit can.

The strangers saw this as they hurriedly stopped the truck and ran back to survey the damage.

"What do you think we should do?" one asked despondently.

"Well, I don't know about you, but I'm relieved," his buddy said. "I could never plow behind a mule going that fast, anyhow."

LUCIFER AND THE COW MONEY

That summer when it happened I was 10 and Bennie 11. And Lucifer, Bennie's tame crow, he must have been two or three. I loved that crow dearly and begged Bennie to sell him to me, but Bennie wouldn't, and I couldn't blame him for he thought the world of Lucifer, too.

I lived with my mother, sister and brother in a small town on the southern fringe of the Uwharries. Bennie, my cousin, lived on a farm out in the country. I visited him as often as school and my mother would permit. During summer school vacations, I'd spend weeks with him, helping on the farm.

Those were great times, the kind every man experienced in his youth and cherishes in his memory. Every day was a bright adventure and every night found two tired boys with stories to tell and futures to talk about before relaxing to sweet and healthy slumber.

And there was Lucifer to brighten those days and to wake up in the night laughing about.

Lucifer was a talking crow. That is, he could say two understandable words: "Raise hell." A neighbor of Bennie's, old man Lou Chavers, had been around Lucifer when the crow was at an impressionable age and those two were favorites of old man Lou's. Somehow Lucifer latched onto them and they were the only articulate sounds we could coax out of him.

What made it distressing was that Lucifer was totally indiscriminate about when and where he used his two words.

Some men sawmilling in the Uwharries had given Lucifer to Bennie when he was only a wobbly little bundle of feathers that had come squawking down out of the nest when the men felled the pine tree that had been his birthplace. They slit the young crow's tongue. "Maybe he'll talk for you when he gets older, son," they told Bennie.

But the two words old man Lou had bequeathed him were the only civilized utterances that Lucifer seemed to care about learning. Bennie and I learned to interpret more of his squawks and screeches than anyone else, but a lot of time we were wrong and we found the crow to be erratic and inconsistent.

Neurotic, Aunt Martha called him. She dreaded the sight of him. "Bennie's Black Bird," she called him when he behaved; otherwise he was the "Black Bandit." She just barely tolerated him and that was all.

Uncle Willie would hardly tolerate him. Although he laughed at the crow's antics, whenever Lucifer got in his hair, literally or figuratively, he'd get hopping mad and go looking for his shotgun and Bennie and I would have to keep Lucifer out of sight until he cooled off.

Lucifer got sadistic enjoyment out of frightening strangers. Sometimes, the church ladies from town would visit Aunt Martha and they'd sit outside in the summer day in the cool of the predusk hour. If Lucifer wasn't around, we'd find him and fling him on the group.

He'd fly aloft and, like a dive bomber gone mad, come screaming down at the ladies shouting his two-word vocabulary. He'd pull out of his dive just before knocking off their hats. He never had to make a second run. One created enough pandemonium. The ladies shrieked and stampeded for the house. Hidden behind the woodpile or the scuppernong arbor, Bennie and I laughed until our sides hurt and tears streamed down our faces. We made the most of it, because Aunt Martha's retaliation was severe.

If the visitors weren't strangers and Lucifer wasn't in a militant mood, like as not he'd put on a show. He was a real exhibitionist. He loved to perform before a crowd and people would come to Uncle Willie's for miles in hopes of catching Lucifer in one of his whimsical moods.

He could outmaneuver any jet fighter you've ever seen. He'd

float along gracefully doing slowrolls, barrelrolls, loops, blackflops and other aerial gymnastics I've never seen equalled to this day.

The falling leaf exercise was a sort of speciality of his and he seemed to get a big kick out of doing it. He'd position his wings rigidly and float down in that rocking back and forth motion exactly like a falling, breeze-stirred leaf. Sometimes he'd squawk and garble as he descended. And sometimes, he'd say "raise hell" much to the discomfort of the young men and women and church people. When he got started, he'd say it over and over again.

Lucifer got pure delight from scaring the sparrows. On cold, drizzling days in the fall and winter, scores of the little sparrows took shelter in the matted branches of the huge cedar tree in the edge of the yard. There in the thick foliage they were safe from the cold and drizzle. But not from Lucifer.

He'd fly high in the air and like a black meteor come blasting down at the cedar. By the time he rocketed down by the side of the tree, he'd be making all the noise he could muster, like a thousand screaming banshees.

The little birds were nearly scared out of their feathers. They fell out of the cedar and fluttered to the naked branches of nearby trees where they sat and chirped lamentably. Since there was no other shelter close by, they gradually crept back into the big cedar. Lucifer watched slyly from afar. When most of them got settled back in the cedar, he did a repeat performance and kept the poor little birds frightened and frustrated all day.

I grew to love that crow with a passion. I yearned to possess him. Visiting Bennie every weekend wasn't enough. I began to feel bitter toward Uncle Willie and Aunt Martha for wanting to do away with Lucifer.

But he grew meaner and became much more of a nuisance with advancing age. His rascality, however, did not lessen my adoration for him. I would have gladly given everything I owned for that crow.

He blinded Aunt Martha's pet cat, old "Jule," by a vicious attack with his claws. Then one day, he took a hunk out of Bennie's finger. He began to steal things from the porch. He would even invade the house if a door or window was left open and come flying out with his claws full of loot.

Aunt Martha missed a golden locket that had belonged to her

great grandmother. A picture in a small antique frame that she prized highly disappeared. Uncle Willie saw Lucifer fly off the back porch with a string of dried red pepper one day.

He got so he would pull pieces of wash off the clothes line, terrorize the chickens and attack visiting children.

The inevitable happened. Bennie and I had been wondering how long Uncle Willie would put up with it. We tried our best to rationalize Lucifer's behavior. But Uncle Willie wouldn't listen. Not after what happened that Saturday morning in May.

I remember it well. I hitched a ride out from town that Friday after school with a neighbor who'd been to mill. Leaving his wagon at the village crossroads, I took a shortcut across the woods to Bennie's place.

They were in a gay frame of mind that evening, Uncle Willie and Aunt Martha, blithe and jolly. Bennie glowed.

There was good reason for jubilance in the household. Uncle Willie had just that morning sold a cow and a calf for $72, a tidy sum in that day.

I drifted off to sleep that night with Bennie talking about ships, pirates and treasures. Next morning he was gone when I awoke. We were just sitting down to breakfast when he came in. "I was seeing about Jezziebell and her litter," he explained.

Uncle Willie, Bennie and I were planting cotton in the crabapple field later that morning when Aunt Martha came running toward us.

"It's gone! It's gone! "she screamed. She was frantic. Her thin, wrinkled face was hysterical. "The money. The crow got it. I left the window open for the room to air out. I was coming back from the spring and saw that Black Bandit fly out with something white in his bill."

That's the way it happened. They'd left the $72 in a white envelope tucked in the family Bible lying on the dresser in the bedroom. Aunt Martha saw Lucifer fly out the window with something white in his beak. She ran and looked and the money was gone.

Uncle Willie tied the mules to a pasture post and went to the house and got his gun.

"I'll kill him for this," he said, his face white and tense.

"Let us try to find him first, Uncle Willie," I begged.

"Maybe we can find that place where he keeps all that stuff he's been taking from the house," Bennie said.

But Uncle Willie wouldn't promise. He just stood there in the yard with the shotgun cradled in his arm and his eyes searched for the crow.

"Give us a chance to find him, please," Bennie and I called as we headed for the woods.

We searched for an hour in the woods and thickets on all sides of the house without avail. Heading back for the house, we were walking by the foot of Laurel Bank, a rocky, laurel-studded bluff near the creek. Bennie looked pale and worried. I was tired and anxious. My eyes glimpsed a dark hole amid some rocks on the face of the bluff near some bushes. There were some objects around the hole and one of them looked familiar, but I was too far away to identify it. I stopped and turned to Bennie to announce my discovery.

But at that instant, the thunder of a shotgun came from the house.

"He's shot Lucifer!" Bennie squalled, a sob clogging his throat, a wildness glistening in his dark eyes.

He jumped over a log, splashed across the cold creek waters and took off up across the hill for the house. I took another look at that hole and followed him. My heart already was sinking toward my shoes.

Not much was left of Lucifer but a bloody mess of feathers.

Uncle Willie put a gnarled hand on Bennie's shoulder. "Hated to have to do it, son," he said. "I knowed you boys thought a lot of him. But he was getting too bold and too mean. It was better this way."

We wrapped the remains in a burlap sack and took it down below the spring to the family burying ground. I spaded out a hole in the damp earth while Bennie sat with head downcast. I knew he would cry his eyes out when I left for I did the same thing when I got away from there. A great sense of vengeance overwhelmed me.

Losing the money was a blow to the folks but they got by without too much hardship. Uncle Willie died a few years later. Bennie went off to school. The last I heard, Aunt Martha was living comfortably with her grandchildren. I haven't heard from Bennie in many years now.

After high school and military service, I wrote my way into journalism, a trade I've followed ever since. I sit to open my middle desk drawer and reach inside. My fingers close over a musty yellowed envelope. There are greenbacks inside. I don't have to to count them. There are seven tens and two ones in that envelope.

Yes, I found the place where Lucifer stashed his loot. Found it on my way back home later that morning before Uncle Willie and a bunch of his neighbors started combing the woods in an effort to locate the envelope with the cow money which they presumed Lucifer had dropped somewhere in the woods. Funny thing about that place, too .

That sheltered cleft in the rocks on Laurel Bank contained many small things that Lucifer undoubtedly did fly there with from the house – such as one of Uncle Willie's stiff white collars that Aunt Martha could have easily mistaken for the envelope. But there were other things that Lucifer couldn't possibly have brought. Like an old axe and spade, a flat iron with a chunk broken out of the handle, a thick roll of burlap bags, and that box about the size of a suitcase.

It was a crudely built wooden box with a cheap padlock on it. I used the axe to bust into it. Inside is where I found the envelope with the cow money. There were other things, one of which I recognized as Aunt Martha's golden locket.

This is where Bennie had been that morning when I woke up and he was gone. He and Lucifer shared a common cache for their loot from the house. But Bennie had let Lucifer take the rap – had let him die – for a crime that he had committed. He didn't get to enjoy the fruits of his crime, though.

I took the money. I didn't tell anyone about anything I had found or seen. It was a mean trick. But it was my way of getting even with Uncle Willie. And with Bennie, for they grilled Bennie for weeks after the search party found the cache on Laurel Bank and the broken wooden box. Whether he ever confessed, I don't know, but it probably stigmatized him for life among his relatives.

The cow money lay untouched until some lean years when it helped me make ends meet. I kept the envelope. As soon as it was financially convenient, I returned the full amount to the envelope just as it was the day when I found it in the box on that Uwharrie hillside. It's been right with me ever since.

I tuck the envelope back in its niche in the corner and close the drawer. I intend to leave the money there forever. I walk over to the window and contemplate my image on the glass surface.

I know I did wrong. I know it's too late now...but I'm sorry for what I did, Uncle Willie.

NATURE'S
MYSTERY MAN OF FIGURES

Nature designed Jonse Mauney for figuring and little else. A human forerunner of the electronic computers of today, the illiterate man had whirring mathematical wheels in his head and a built-in memory timepiece which functioned infallibly. Throughout his 50-odd years in his native Uwharrie village of New London, he never satisfied the strange cravings of his figure-hungry mind, though he digested mountains of figures by the hour.

All it took to energize Jonse was to feed him figures. Torrents of figures. For as long as you cared. And just as fast as they came in he'd spout them back at you – any way you wanted them – totaled, multiplied, squarerooted, averaged, reversed, or juggled in any special way. He ran them through the unknown rollers of his mind and squeezed out every angle. He played with them in every possible combination and pattern. Then, on request, he recited them back in the original order.

Though he could read figures, Jonse couldn't write them. All his answers were oral. To him a pen or pencil was only a plaything for making meaningless marks.

Jonse stood beside the railroad near his home and absorbed the long row of numbers on each of the score or more of freight cars which whizzed past. Soon as the last car passed, Jonse could give you the total of all the numbers.

One forgotten trainman posed this question: If it takes a locomotive drive wheel 14 feet to make one complete turn, how many turns would it make in, say 2,803.7 miles? Jonse began rattling off the answer hardly before the flabbergasted man finished stating his problem.

Someone tossed this puzzler at him which he purportedly answered forthwith: How many ticks would a clock make in two months, two weeks, three days, seven hours, 14 minutes, and 36 seconds of steady ticking?

Typical of the questions asked Jonse was this one posed by the late Brack Talbert of New London back in 1909. If he had started out by horseback on the 93-million-mile journey to the sun at the beginning of the year 1 A.D. and had maintained a steady rate of travel since, how far would he be toward his destination? Jonse's answer, someone remembers, showed that Talbert would have covered only about one-sixth of the distance to the sun.

Delighted school kids covered their slates with numbers and held them up for Jonse to total at a glance.

In less time than it takes to sneeze, Jonse told one middle-aged man how old he was in months, how old he was in weeks, in days, in hours, in minutes, even in seconds. Huge concentrations of similar objects fascinated Jonse. They say he could, with a sweep of his eyes, almost count the hairs on your head, stars in the sky, the kernels of grain in the wheat bin.

When asked the answer to a perplexing riddle of figures, Jonse seldom hesitated. Occasionally he lowered his big head and pawed his jaw with a thumb before he spoke. Folks remember that he sometimes had to catch his breath several times before he finished reciting a long answer.

Jonse could not explain how he made his lightning computations. He never attempted to. The answers just seemed to click into place on some gigantic register in his head while the question was being asked. The nearest he ever came to explaining his power was the time he allegedly confided to a white friend that the ability "came to" him one day in his youth while he cut cordwood in the forest and watched the numberless branches of the trees slashing in the wind.

"It was a gift," the villagers said of his figuring ability.

Many people still live today who remember Jonse and his colossal figuring feats.

No clue to Jonse's gift can be ascertained from the standpoint of heredity. His father was "Uncle" Cad Mauney and his mother "Aunt" Hettie Mauney was only 14 years older than her son. They were former slaves. Jonse himself was born in slavery. None of his several brothers and sisters had any impressive talents.

While they amused themselves with Jonse's eccentricities, people harnessed his gift for practical purposes, too.

Notable among these were the country store merchants of the vicinity who, at inventory or reckoning time, sat Jonse down on the counter with a licorice stick to nibble on and turned him into an adding machine. By quoting prices and statistics to him they figured up their assets and liabilities, their turnover in goods and dollars, and their total worth, and how long it would take them to make a million dollars.

His genius with figures brought visitors from distant places who plied him with tricky questions. Their skepticism seared, they lingered to marvel at this incredible man and his effortless answers which withstood whatever acid test anyone cared to make on them. Never was he known to be wrong.

Tradition has it that professors and scientists from famous institutions came and observed the phenomenon of Jonse and went away shaking their heads.

Jonse is said to have refused lucrative offers from show business to travel and demonstrate his mathematical wizardry. Likewise he turned down a plea from a large New York company for him to come and let them funnel all their figuring and statistical work through his head.

Villagers said Jonse always stayed pretty close to nature. They observed him standing motionless while watching thick snowflakes swirl down, listening intently to the patter of rain on the roof, absorbed by the lively song of a bird, transfixed by the pliable sod tumbling from the plow, by the rustle of leaves and the slither of creek water over rocks, by the rumble and growl of thunder. He seemed to try to capture and interpret nature's symphonies and to translate these things into figures which his mind could grasp and assimilate.

Somehow he must have succeeded, too. For whenever you met Jonse he was mumbling figures to himself from the unquenchable numerical gusher in his head. His staccato mumble ceased only when you interrupted by speaking to him.

Other than his early cordwood cutting, Jonse's only gainful employment was working at odd jobs. And here another startling peculiarity became recognized. You could hire Jonse to rake your leaves or chop your wood for a certain specified length of time – say one hour and 39 minutes – and he always stopped right on the dot although he never had a timepiece. People actually timed him.

Probably the most enjoyment Jonse got out of life was reminding his townspeople of their birthdays and anniversaries. If you once told him your birth date he never forgot. If you had been born locally within his life span he already had your redletter days filed away in his prodigious memory. He could tell you the year, month, day, the hour, even the prevailing weather conditions at the time of the momentous event and relate it to some local happening of significance. The sight of his shuffling hulk at the back door meant an anniversary was due right away in the home.

Georgia M. Haswell, former head of the Department of Mathematics of Pfeiffer College, Misenheimer, N.C., has studied the record of Jonse. She comments:

"What is so amazing to me is his rapidity at applying the elementary operations of mathematics and his remarkable memory in retaining partial sums and products to be used in the next steps. Just what combination of brain cells enable a man to do this we do not know. We do know there are people with this unusual gift. We can only observe and wonder, not explain."

Nature called again one cold winter day in March of 1915 and Jonse answered. The decades have obliterated all signs of his grave in the cemetery west of the village. Snowflakes fell thick and fast the day they buried him. No one knew, of course, but folks figured old Jonse died on time, too.